C000263721

Macbeth Speaks 1997

A Woman of Some Importance

Hello, Juno Speaking

by

J ohn Cargill Thompson

diehard
Edinburgh

diehard
publishers
3 Spittal Street
Edinburgh
EH3 9DY

ISBN 0 946230 26 9

Copyright John Cargill Thompson 1997

British Library Cataloguing in Publication Data
A catalog record for this book is
available from the British Library

Other **diehard** drama

Klytemnestra's Bairns, Bill Dunlop
Cutpurse/Once in Beaucaire, Bill Dunlop
Hare and Burke, Owen Dudley Edwards
Gang Doun wi a Sang, a play about William Soutar, by Joy Hendry
Port and Lemon, the mystery behind Sherlock Holmes/*Laird of Samoa*, John Cargill Thompson (out of print)
Cheap and Tearful/Feel Good, John Cargill Thompson (out of print)
What Shakespeare Missed/Romeo & Juliet: Happily Never After/The Marvellous Boy/Cock-a-doodle-do! by John Cargill Thompson (out of print)
A Matter of Conviction/Parting Shot/When the Rain Stops, by John Cargill Thompson (out of print)
The Lord Chamberlain's Sleepless Nights, a collection of plays by John Cargill Thompson (out of print)
Everything in "The Garden" and other plays, by John Cargill Thompson
Hamlet II: prince of Jutland/Macbeth Speaks/An English Education, by John Cargill Thompson (out of print)
Uncorking Old Sherry/Queen Hester/A Gentleman of England, by John Cargill Thompson
Jezebel, Every Inch a King, Clever Boy, Guerilla, by John Cargill Thompson
Lucky Numbers, Richard III for Windows, King of the Commons, by John Cargill Thompson
Soul Doubt, Lear: A Mythconception, Bloody Heart, by John Cargill Thompson
Alcestis & Medea by George Buchanan (in Latin)
Jephthes & Baptistes by George Buchanan (in Latin)
Cruising by John Herdman

to Jessica

Macbeth Speaks 1997

"Macbeth Speaks" (or as it was then called "Macbeth: the Alternative Version") was originally written in 1984 and was the third of my one person plays. It was not performed until 1991 in a shortened version as part of a double bill with "A Matter of Conviction". I then revised the text for publication in 1995. All previous versions omitted Macbeth's visit to Rome in 1050, because the historical significance of this conflicted with my original agenda which was to create an entertainment which could be used as part of a Theatre in Education programme for students studying Shakespeare's play. I now believe that there should be no compromise between Shakespeare's glorious fantasy and the story of the last High King of Scots.

> This Macbeth whilk wis baith wise and wight
> Strang in ane stour and true as ony stull:
> Defender also of the common weal.
> So just ane judge, so equel and so true,
> As by his deeds richt weal before all show.
>
> William Stewart (after Hector Boece) 1531.

Macbeth Speaks 1997

This play should be set and designed as for a production of Shakespeare's 'Macbeth'. Ideally I would prefer to have three actors perform the opening scene, although I am aware that costs may necessitate the lines being recorded; if the latter then scene one should be presented in a black out.

First Witch: When shall we three meet again
In thunder, lightning, or in rain?

Second Witch: When the hurly burly's done,
When the battle's lost and won.

Third Witch: That will be ere the set of sun.

First Witch: Where the place?

Second Witch: Upon the heath.

All: There to meet with Macbeth.

Second Witch: Macbeth.

Third Witch: Macbeth.

Exeunt Witches.

Macbeth Enters through the audience handing out pebbles to its members. He wears a simple brown monkish robe, suggesting the hermit rather than the warrior. His feet are bare.

Macbeth: Go on my dear have a stone on me ... you? ... perhaps you then? ... No.

Chuckles

Isn't a bad reputation a terrible thing ... people won't share stones with you, eh?

Laughs

1

Sorry! ... I can't help it, you all look so totally confused. Where do stones come into Macbeth, eh?

That's the trouble they don't! Not according to William Shakespeare.

Put 'em away ... but don't lose them ... they are a clue.

Blesses them in such a way as to provoke an ambiguous response.

Bona dies et pax vobiscum.

Why do you start and seem to fear things that do sound so fair?

Translates what he has just said.

Good day and the peace of God be with you.
God ... God ... God!

Yes, I have named my God and I am still here ... no red flash and a little yellow demon at my elbow to carry me back to hell.

And it's working, isn't it?
It is! You are confused.
Not your idea of Macbeth at all.
Pebbles and Paternosters.

But you see, that is just what it is about ... Stones and how to pray ... You can forget this anthology *(produces a copy of the play)* of bogeys and bewitchment ... The boy done well ... but it's not true ... Ay, the boy's done too bloody well hasn't he?

> "Macbeth was not a good man,
> > he had his little ways,
> And sometimes no one spoke to him
> > for days and days and days
> At Christmas time the cards of cheer,
> > that stood upon his shelf,
> Were never from his near and dear,
> > but only from himself!"

Let's start with the facts:

> "The strong one was fair, brown haired and tall,
> Very pleasant was the handsome youth to me
> Brimful of food was Scotland East and West,
> During the reign of the ruddy, the brave King."

That is contemporary ... well give or take fifty years ... It's about the only contemporary account that does survive ... I lost, remember, Shakespeare got that bit right ... and the winners write the record books ... But even creative history cannot ignore "Brimful of food was Scotland East and West" ... Twenty-three years of peace and prosperity ... Ay, it was really rather a dull time ... sorry! No murders, no magic, no kinky sex ... There was a little scandal about a shepherd in Sutherland ... but apart from that it was simple harmonious living ... "Brimful of food was Scotland East and West during the reign of the ruddy, the brave King." ... And I must be very careful here, mustn't I?

Macbeth has become a tradition ... Come on, disappoint a tradition and anything can happen ... oh yes, disappoint people in their expectations and what's left, eh?

> Well what is left?
> Fear and superstition.
> This!
> The play you know and love.

> "When shall we three meet again?
> In thunder, lightning, or in rain?"

Frightened people can unloose a deal of uncontrolled energy ... oh ay, begin thinking scary and something scary will happen.

That is what happened.
To me.
It is, you know!
The rest of the world was thinking scared and poor old Macbeth got caught in the ebb.

Throw this away, it's havers.

You know nothing ... not even the year I came to the throne ... Oh, don't worry about it ... I'd have been very surprised if any of you knew that ... Not like 55 BC and 1066 ... your conquerors wouldn't let you forget those, eh? ... no, forget those and you might remember what it is to be free.

I came to the throne in 1034 AD.
Exactly!

One thousand years after the White Christ died on Golgotha to redeem you all ... one thousand years after the most significant event in Christian history ... the Passion of Our Lord Jesu Christ ... Believe me, there was some fear in the world then ... everybody thinking "This ... is ... it! ... Second-Coming Time ...

That is if He isn't here already" ... Stern vikings who've spent half a lifetime in a veritable orgy of pillage, rape and arson, falling over themselves to get to the few churches they've left standing for a splash about in the Holy Water and a new name ... You go up to some punter whom you've known from the cradle as Thorkyll Bear Slayer, and he tells you he is now called Emmanuel and doing voluntary work on behalf of the berserkers' reformation society ... "Would I like to make a contribution?" ... More altars collapse under the weight of all the swords and battle axes being exchanged for strings of little brown rosary beads than the last ten centuries have seen off in honest heathen havoc.

Don't worry about it ... There's no problem ... Employment for all, eh? ... Building bigger and better churches ... oh yes, the Church offers shelter ... well, to Christendom ... everybody else is scared shitless, but Christendom is sheltered.

So what's gone wrong?
Hadrian's bloody wall.
Confused again?

Because of Hadrian's wall we Scots are not sure if we are in Christendom or not ... you see we'd joined before you lot when all the rules and regulations hadn't been fully negotiated ... and we weren't paying the same dues as everyone else ... our monks ... we call them culdees ... walk in the footsteps of Padraig and Callum ... Patrick and Columba to you ... not Peter and Paul.

Yes ... that makes us even more vulnerable than our friends the Odin worshippers, eh? ... they at least have beastly habits to give up and be amnestied for.

We Celts ... ooh! ... we are doing really naughty things aren't we?

Celebrating Easter on a different day.

No tonsures.

Our priests getting married and having children instead of getting a bit on the side from their housekeeper.

The Celtic Church didn't have any property.

Come on, a Christian Church without possessions, a church that gives rather than takes, it's not on, is it?

Still got those stones I gave you? ... pass them round ... you were beginning to wonder when they were going to come in, weren't you?

4

We did have buildings ... but they were functional ... For our great festivals we prefer to gather in the old tribal places.

Exactly ... The stone circles of our ancestors.

We haven't a clue about their original purpose ... why should that bother us for God's sake? ... Our Christianity isn't jealous of anything that has gone on before it ... They are our heritage, we know there cannot be anything bad about that.

What is an altar? ... Just a slab of stone, eh? ... The same stuff you are passing round only bigger ... No, we are not superstitious about stones, superstition comes with guilt ... we just appreciate the comfort they can give.

Come on, who hasn't picked up pebbles on the sea shore, eh? ... and then spent one of those marvellous silly evenings sorting and re-sorting them ... ay, and if you've a sibling quarrelling over the best ones ... not bad quarrels, fun quarrels, with cuddles for making up ... we've all got a stone somewhere in the house ... one that we can't bring ourselves to throw out, eh? ... It's been there since you were a child.

Yes, I had one ... a great big family stone ... called the Lia Fail ... The Stone of Destiny ... It was big enough to sit on.

Ay, when I sat on the Lia Fail, I was conscious not only of rubbing arses with all my progenitors, but that I was in direct contact with the bones of Mother Scotland.

And they lost it ... They lost the Lia Fail.
How can anyone lose a stone that big?

Very easily if you've forgotten what it means ... if it isn't a family stone anymore ... just one that has been left behind by the punters who were living here before you.

God, I'm getting gloomy ... Come on, let's have some more light on all this and to hell with bogeys and bewitchment ... you shouldn't make love in the dark.

As lights come up he reacts in mock surprise.

Oh yes, I try to keep up ... of course I do, I am a civilised being ... I have an enquiring mind ... but it is very difficult to fully appreciate the wonders of a culture that is not your own ... I mean, one always thinks one has got it right, doesn't one?

Pointing to the lights

To me that is just a smidgen suspicious ... Light for the asking ... command our night and day ... I don't understand it ... it must be witchcraft ... or extreme sanctity ... Oh yes, in my time you either got burnt or made a saint if you could do things like that ... There was a laddie ... but to hell with him, you can all do it now, can't you? ... just by pushing a piece of plastic ...

Looks closely at the audience

No! ... You are not all saints, are you? ... you certainly aren't, I know that smile ... don't waste it on me, I'm a married man.

Yes ... man.

Take my hand if you don't believe me ... go on, take it ... Well, tell them ... my flesh doesn't burn with the fires of hell, does it? ... Possibly it's a bit sweaty ... that's natural ... I'm scared of you ... Face of Christ, I'd rather stand in the shield linden waiting for your bloody ancestors to erupt out of the mist than be here on my own trying to tell you about something that not only doesn't exist any more, but has been replaced by one of the greatest plays ever written ...

> "Tomorrow, and tomorrow, and tomorrow,
> Creeps in this petty pace from day to day
> To the last syllable of recorded time ... "

Marvellous!

It says here in the introduction that if Shakespeare hadn't written it I would be forgotten ... Here it is!

> "Just an obscure murdering little kinglet
> unremembered even in his own country"

> "Brimful of food was Scotland East and West,
> During the reign of the ruddy, the brave King."

I was Ard Righ n'h'Alba. High King of Scots.

And that's just words ... King? ... High King? ... so what?

I did not succeed because I was someone's son ... or because I killed someone's son ... I didn't oppress, rape or interfere with people's sheep ... I was elected to my place by men and women, ay, women, nuns are a Roman institution ... men and women who had as much right to it as I had ... oh yes ... the Ard Righ was the elected guardian of a set of traditions that go right back to when we gave the Romans, poor bastards, such a hard time, they had to build a bloody great wall and order everybody to start pretending that the world ended there.

Oh yes, that's when it all started.
Your confusion.

The great Celtic Empire that comes down to you in charming little fantasies about Arthur, Morgan le Fey and the Lady Guinevere ... traded with Tyre and Zidon, with Egypt and Troy ... There was tin from this Island in Solomon's temple ... But the Romans told you we were a bunch of savages ... and Romans know best ... Well they are such decent chaps and they have given you a civilisation ... You owe them a lot ... all Europe does ... after all it's Rome that made the world possible for Christianity ... your kind of Christianity ... she created the framework ... Christendom was just an extension of Rome ... why do you think the Pope lives there?

Have you got it yet?
The difference between my world and yours?

I'm so obviously inferior, eh? ... I've not had the benefit of a classical education ... oh yes, it took us Gaels and Celts that wee bit longer to find out all about those fascinating Roman gods and goddesses, you know, the ones with the exotic tastes in swans, bulls, and bondage ... ay, those ones, the ones that make sheep and welly boots seem normal.

Far from being a "petty murdering kinglet" ... I was High King of a confederation that stretched almost as far south as Greater Manchester ... and if any of you have ever been to Manchester you'll appreciate why we stopped there ... you can take the responsibility for civilising people so far and no further, eh?

Back to the introduction to the play, as if reading from it.

"An ambitious, self centred man seduced by evil visions and his wife's strength of will into killing his overlord ... finally destroyed by the very forces to which he as surrendered."

That is so Roman
So bloody clear cut.
A conflict between good and evil ... with good very concerned about property and power ... ay, and possessions ... Don't you see, I didn't have any power ... at least not by some divine right

... I had responsibility ... of course I had possessions ... even Lenin had his own underpants ... but I wasn't obsessive about them ... How do I explain our sharings? ... You know how families can be very jealous of some things ... "Who's pockled the last cream cake, eh? ... That was mine!" ... but others are held in comfortable common? ... You see we hadn't had our natural generosity confused by conquest ... we didn't have one race of rulers and another of ruled ... oh yes, that's how important beating Rome had been for us ... w didn't have a class system ... we were all warriors and we were all peasants ... ay, even the Ard Righ ... I had to work in the fields just like everyone else.

It's a dream now, isn't it? ... perhaps it wasn't really like that at all ... because of course we did have our fair share of greedy hubristic bastards ... ay, like my cousin Duncan ... but we were certainly not, I assure you, a load of kilted barbarians running round going "Hooch!" all the time like those wallies that used to invade Wembley every two years.

So where does it come from? ... all this blood and witchcraft ... it's so very Scottish isn't it?

> "Warlocks and witches in the mirk,
> By Alloway's auld haunted kirk."

Come on, it's what you all think about whenever anybody mentions 'Macbeth' ... for God's sake, actors go absolutely bananas, clap their hands over their ears and start a frightful ritual that includes pulling each other's noses and turning round in circles with their eyes shut.

Consults play

I wouldn't mind if it was just me ... after all it does have a certain John Wayne ring to it:

> "Till he unseamed him from the nave to the chops
> And fixed his head upon our battlements."

But how can you do this to her? ... How can you do this to my Gruoch? ... You didn't even know she had a name did you? ... It was Gruoch ... it sounds like water gently stroking pebbles ... or the wind caressing heather ... It suited her.

Oh Gruoch, my lady ... granddaughter ... wife and mother of Kings.

How do you picture her?

"................... I have given suck, and know
How tender 'tis to love the babe that milks me;
I would while it was smiling in my face
Have plucked my nipple from his boneless gums
And dashed the brains out, had I so sworn as you
Have done to this."

Oh, it's not Shakespeare's fault ... He didn't even understand
the lie that is being told ... I should thank him, at least he's given
it a kind of dignity.

You are right little man ... I was nothing without Gruoch ...
and I am nothing with her.

Oh yes, I promise you the breath of her night robe bending a
candle flame could make me sweat.

My dear, come here ... Face of God, you are so bloody
beautiful ... hold me ... my mother, my daughter ... my love ...
my friend.

Hey! ... shall I really confuse you now? ... mhm?
Wait for it!
Lady Macbeth is Macduff.
No, I am not just being clever.

Don't you see? ... This story was first told for a far, far more
sinister purpose than an afternoon's theatrical entertainment.

It was told to justify the destruction of a way of life.
It succeeded, didn't it?
Macduff was the King's name.
My name ... Gruoch's name.
For us the chief of Clan Macduff had an almost spiritual
authority. Gruoch was our Chief of Clan Macduff, I told you
women had authority with us.

Do you get it now? ... by inserting a fictional Macduff chief
into the story as one of the leaders of the Junta that deposes me
you gave it instant respectability.

Poor Shakespeare, he never really did understand why it was
so important that I should be killed by Macduff and not Malcolm
... to him it was just a name in the chronicles.

"Beware Macduff!"

That is the Royal name. And the first of that ilk is my wife
Gruoch.

Oh yes, Lady Macbeth is Macduff ... It is in her right and the right of her son Lulach that I have rule.

Ay, we came together at first in convenient friendship and respect.

Oh yes, when I began to realise I loved her I became scared stiff ... I could hardly touch her ... not easily ... love must be giving not taking.

And I am losing my credibility, aren't I? ... what happened between Gruoch and I is none of your business ... but this makes me so bloody angry ... Don't you see, it is what has been done to Gruoch that has torn me out of my grave to come here to speak to you tonight.

You want a fiend-like queen? You want Shakespeare's Lady Macbeth? ... try the wife of my successor ... oh yes, Saint bloody Margaret ... she drove her husband to his death ... she stole common land to endow her church ... but she's a saint because she won.

Gruoch and I reigned peacefully for twenty-three years ... everybody had enough to eat ... Very unnatural ... we must have had some help ... a society without poverty and oppression? It must be witchcraft ... why, it undermines mother church ... The church thrives on poor people.

Read our old Celtic stories ... the ones that have survived Christian revision ... green ... green as the green hills of Erin ... full of strong light and colour ... no witches ... monsters, yes ... monsters to challenge a man's aspiration ... but the little darknesses of diablerie? ... no way I'm afraid.

About the only thing this punter's got right is my name ... Macbeth ... ay, and he even mispronounces it ... It is actually MacVaha ... It mean's son of life, from the same root as usque va ha ... water of life ... ay, whisky ... the connotations are equally ironic, eh?

I am MacVaha ... MacFinlay ... MacRuari ... MacCullen ... MacKenneth ... MacDuff ... yes, Macduff, Macduff, Macduff ... MacDonald ... MacConstantine ... MacKenneth ... MacAlpine.

That's roots.
That's where I come from.

Hardly a murdering usurper, eh? With a pedigree like that I could win prizes at a cattle show.

Ah, but where am I going?

Shall I really confuse you now? I'm going Inter-Railing with my wife. Well there's an irresistible offer for the Christmas holiday period. Anywhere you like in Christendom or New Rome. It doesn't say anything about surcharges but it's still a good offer.

Ay, I'm being flippant, but you see that's the whole point ... I can be.

Scotland is brimful of food from East to West while England on the other hand is in a right mess. Their King, Edward the Confessor is very old and very childless. Everyone is lining up to form the next government.

Everyone, well, everyone except me, has started scheming and killing to succeed him. What is the big deal about being King England? You'd think being a King was a hard enough job without taking on the English balance of trade deficit into the bargain, but they're all after that little padded gold circlet ... Sveyn of Denmark, Harald Norway ... and there's even a few Englishmen like Harold Godwinson who appeal to the Eurosceptics. Ay, England's got its problems. Too many problems to bother about us.

So I can go on holiday.
Ay, abroad.
Thorfinn can look after things while we're away.

And I haven't told you about Thorfinn, have I? This is new stuff, this wasn't on your A level syllabus, so pay attention. He was my cousin and foster brother and he was known as the Raven Feeder so as not to confuse him with his grandfather, Thorfinn Skullcrusher. Names like that tell you why Shakespeare had to leave him out, don't they? If he'd put in Thorfinn he'd have taken over the play. He was Kirk Douglas and Tony Curtis rolled into one ... girls couldn't resist him ... a real viking.

> "Jarl Thorfinn stood by Odin's Tree
> A mighty axe in his hand had he,
> Out! Out!"

You see what I mean, as soon as I start talking about Finn I lose my thread. Do you know there are some people who think he and I were the same person. No, if Thorfinn had ruled Scotland he'd never have lost it, that I promise you.

But do you not realise the wonder of that statement?
"I can go abroad."
Don't you see what it's saying about our country?

In my day a King was a prisoner of his people. They took away his passport when they stuck the crown on his head. The history books give you the impression that we're still a load of semi-naked savages living in caves while the English are beginning the long hard climb back to civilization, but then the history books were written by the English, weren't they? And anyway they still seem to think we're a load of savages, so what's new? The truth is my Scotland is so economically and politically secure that I, the elected Ard Righ n'h'Alba can leave someone else to look after things and go on holiday for eighteen months. I do not know of a High King of Scots who came after me who was able to do anything remotely similar. If they'd tried they wouldn't have had a kingdom to come home to. Take Prince Charlie, eh? No, the only way a King could get to see other airts was by going to war. Hey, maybe that's why our Kings were such contentious bastards, eh? Flodden wasn't an attempt at conquest, no way, all the poor man wanted was a holiday romance and a shot at the duty frees.

... But my Scotland is so secure that Gruoch and I are able to slip away almost unnoticed. For eighteen months we share the world and its wonders, like two teenagers on their honeymoon.

It's great to travel with someone you love, isn't it? You don't have to speak, do you? A look will do. Everything is twice as beautiful and twice as funny. I maun admit if Gruoch had not been with me I'd have been home in half the time. But she was. Nowhere's quite like its neighbour, is it? It's not just the way people build their houses, or pray to their God. You expect that but it just doesn't occur to you that herring tastes different abroad, you think it would be the same wherever you were, but every new town has its secret ingredient to surprise the tongue.

And that's how things should be, isn't it? The wonder of diversity. Christendom would make us all the same. The old things, that made us different and tell us who we are, threaten Christendom.

Ay, that's why we left Scotland. We went to Rome to try to explain to Pope Leo that our stones were no threat to him and very important to us. The Lia Fail may once have been the altar of a pagan god, ay it could very well have been we've had it a very long time. For all I know blood sacrifice was made upon it. It's thousands of years old for God's sake, and it's learnt in those thousand years. It has learnt love and toleration.

And I'm getting sentimental again. Forgive me but walking by the Seine and the Tiber with my arm round the woman I love, or eating foreign sweet meats by the side of a river both of us covered in sugar makes me want to write poetry. In am so free of care. I have this little fantasy that maybe when we get home people will have realised the Raven Feeder's twice the man I am and elected him in my place and Gruoch and I can continue like this.

I love you, my sweet.

Ay, I know it's just a dream, and no we didn't go by Inter-Rail, we joined a pilgrimage, which believe me was just as uncomfortable ... Australians didn't invent back packing.

No privacy and everyone being hearty and singing songs.

No it isn't a holiday, is it? It is my thought that if I can only speak to the Pope man to man maybe I'll be able to persuade him that the date of the Easter Mass isn't worth the destruction of a way of life and I have come myself because I know a priest would end up getting into a silly argument about how many angels can dance on the end of a pin, or indeed whether angels dance at all. Though I'm sure Scottish angels do, eh? No this is something I can't trust to another. This is something I maun do for myself, well with Gruoch, you know what I mean, and we might as well see a little of the world while we're about it. We're not going to get another chance.

Rome is a wonderful place.

Though I must admit I'm a wee bit disappointed in its coast line. It doesn't hold a candle end to the dramatic shores of Scotland. They say the Roman Legionaries hailed the Tay as a second Tiber, they must either have had too much of our whisky or been away from home a gey long time. It's all silted up and not a salmon to be seen, but the City makes up for everything. Ay, it's in ruins but its a marvel in stone. Great columns, some lying across the street, the pavements ornamented with pictures of their gods made with thousands of chips of different coloured stone, bridges, statues. I wish I could have seen it in its glory. I've never seen anything to compare with this, and everywhere cats, accusing cats ... accusing man of neglect. I didn't know there were so many cats in the world. I saw a man urinate on the face of his great-great-grandfather's god, just pull down his breeks and piss on the pavement. I wanted to hit him. In Scotland we have more respect for our past. And I'll tell you something else, the grandeur that was Rome wasn't destroyed by barbarian invaders, oh no, Rome was destroyed by its Popes. They felt threatened by pagan art. And I thought if they could destroy such beauty what hope had Scotland? But it wasn't Leo that did the destroying, was it? That was all in the past.

We stay in a little inn, near where the Spanish Steps are today. We've plenty of time for sight seeing. He canna see us. He's busy. Every day I present myself at the door of the Vatican and every day I get the same answer.

"Come back the morn's morn, maybe he'll see you then."

... that is till somebody tells us we have to pay to see the man, then it is all smiles and "come this way my lord." This is a religion that's gey respectful of its profits.

Still it's worth a little silver to see him. He's a German, from Alsace, and he's as big as Thorfinn, ay he'd make a good viking. This man's a fighter not a bigot. He has to be. In the last seventy five years, twenty eight Popes, one of them only twelve years old have died violent deaths and the twenty ninth who managed somehow to die in his bed alone was dug up a month later by his successor and thrown into the Tiber. Being Pope is not a job for a weakling.

He gets straight down to the business.

When I begin to greet him as I've been instructed, well almost as I've been instructed, I'm not going to kiss any man's big toe whoever he is, he stops me in mid flow.

"Your faith does not accept of my office."

So much for the courtesies and I tell him I accept his holiness as Bishop of Rome. I accept his power.

And he laughs.

"Ay, you want my power on your side, King."

I nod.

"Why should I support you against my own bishops."
"Well, why?"

And I try to explain that the English bishops are not after souls but land and power. Once acknowledge the spiritual supremacy of York and Durham and within fifty years we'll have the English King claiming temporal overlordship of Scotland, ay and claiming it with an army.

As I said he's a German from Alsace. He has no love for the English, and we do a deal. Orkney and Sutherland shall be his, they are already, but under a Norwegian archbishop and he'll instruct York and Durham to stop bothering us.

We shake arms man to man. Then he blesses me and gives me a gold arm ring. I told you he would have made a good viking.

I feel so optimistic as we start for home. The peace we have so carefully built over the last twenty years seems secure at last. I know I can trust this man. For ever and ever as we say when we are children or at prayer. We say it in order to make it so. For ever and ever at peace.

But peace makes awful dull reading does it not?
Let's spice things up a little for the sake of the story.

That's still the problem, isn't it? Shakespeare's history is more dramatic than mine. It may be all a lie but it is such a wonderful dramatic lie.

All hail Macbeth that shall be King hereafter.

I mean what about Banquo, a bit of a wimp part, isn't it? Even when it is combined with Siward to save money on actors. Sorry, he's just a fantasy, like the witches, the invention of a family without roots. Oh ay, he doesn't come into the story for two hundred years, then when the Stewarts need some genuine Celtic street cred and a tartan he turns up.

Lesser then Macbeth, and greater
Not so happy, yet much happier.
Thou shalt get kings, though thou be none.

Well that's one way of stealing a crown. Invent the right ancestors.

This is my problem, isn't it? There's so little relationship between historical truth and this play there's really no point in my trying to compare the two. There isn't, you'll just get even more confused.

You do appreciate this saintly King I'm supposed to kill ... wasn't ... wasn't a King ... well not of Scots ... he was under King of the Welsh of Cumbria.

Oh yes, it was Duncan who rebelled against me ... I am Duncan as well as Macduff.

I'm right aren't I? I've confused you again.

I think we'd better forget the play, eh? It's served its purpose. It got you here, didn't it?

Sorry, there is no mystery and no murder. Prince Duncan was killed by the Raven Feeder in a rather scrappy sea battle off the coast of Fife. I wasn't within a hundred miles of the place. I get sea sick. I'd just have got in the way.

Oh Duncan had a claim. A good one. He'd every right to be a wee bit disappointed. We all thought he was going to be King. That was the problem, so did he, and he took his election for granted. We Scots don't like people who take elections for granted. How many Tory M.P.'s are there exactly? But yes, my grandfather, the King, wanted Duncan to succeed him, that's why he got him elected under King of Cumbria.

But grandfather is dead.

And my fellows surprise everybody by electing me, on the understanding that I will be succeeded not by my own son Fergus, another character Shakespeare had to leave out because you just cannot have a tyrant who's also a loving father, not in a tragic drama, but by my stepson Lulach. We Scots don't like dynasties.

Ay, it was I that was elected Ard Righ.
Duncan didn't like that.
My election made him very, very angry.
And so he invaded England.

That's surprised you, hasn't it? Come on, admit it, you were expecting me to say "Prince Duncan gathers together an army and marches northward." He wasn't a fool. That would have been rebellion.

Oh no, what he did was almost Byzantine in its complexity ... brilliant! You see only a de facto King can invade the territories of another de facto king. Private individuals just raid. Only Kings make war. The implication of Duncan's action is that Scotland is making war on England ... he says he's King of Scots and he's got eight thousand battle axes to back him up ... that's one way of getting your claim recognised. It doesn't really matter that he is beaten and has to take to his ships. It doesn't even matter that his eldest son Malcolm is captured ... in fact in a way it's all to the good ... the English have a different system to us ... as far as they are concerned Kings are succeeded by their eldest sons ... They honestly believe that they have captured the next King of Scots ... ay, and after Thorfinn's done the business they think they've got the King. There now follows twenty-three years of peace and prosperity ... Malcolm grows up ... in England ... what is it the Jesuits say? ... Give us a lad till he's seventeen and he's ours for life ... The boy is English ... give him his due he really does genuinely believe that because he's the son of a King he must be a King ... They take their titles so terribly seriously ... For twenty-three years he grows up ... they are very nice to him ... a good allowance ... dogs ... girls ... everything a healthy lad could desire ... and he grows more bitter every day ... you see there is one thing they won't give him ... an army ... They won't give him one, but they keep hinting that they might one day ... He's such a marvellous weapon.

So what happened?
I've told you.

Christendom was scared of us because we were different ... Everyone else, every square foot of land is accounted for ... our common ownership could give peasants ideas ... ay, and our church is far too free ... we actually talk about the meaning of God and the fallibility of his ministers ... we were definitely a threat ... you can't have different systems ... it undermines society.

The irony of it is the end was almost an accident. Leo didn't break his promise ... nobody actually made a dramatic decision to make war on the Celtic system. England had a problem ... Siward, Earl of Northumberland ... yes, the fellow in the play ... it doesn't do him justice ... he was another of these charismatic viking chappies ... like Thorfinn and that lad Thorkyll Bear Slayer I told you about. The problem is he is refusing to trade in his battle axe ... he doesn't want a string of little brown rosary beads ... he wants to kill people ... I see your point, as far as you are concerned it is much better that he should kill Scots than other Englishmen ... so you lend him to Malcolm who is still asking for an army.

Twenty-three years of peace and prosperity up the spout because of an uncontrollable berserk.

We beat him.

Shakespeare's put two campaigns into one ... I told you to forget the play ... we beat Siward ... but the English have suddenly found a marvellous outlet for their aggressive elements ... so when a punter called Tostig Godwinson ... a brother of that chap Harold that got beaten by William the conqueror ... becomes a little over aggressive and ends up raping a nun ... they lend him to Malcolm ... Can't lose can you? ... you either get your undesirable elements killed off for you or you conquer Scotland.

We weren't expecting them.
Not a second time.
Not so soon.

We are slow to muster ... we won so easily last year, time to get the crops in.

Where's Finn?

I don't believe it. Thorfinn Raven Feeder's got religion ... he's been born again in the Roman faith, that Norwegian archbishop's got to him. He's given up being a viking ... instead of standing on a raised shield firing up his huscarles he's on his knees playing with a string of little brown rosary beads.

All right, retreat.
The further we lure them into these mountains the easier the job will be.

And I make a fatal mistake.

Oh it's a sound enough strategy, stretch their line of communications to breaking point.

The only problem is I should have given orders to have the country they must pass through laid waste ... I should have left them nothing they can possibly make any use of ... not even a bloody egg.

I can't do it ... I can't bring myself to ask people to destroy their children's food.

We'll still beat them ... it's only a bloody raiding party for God's sake ... even God's against them, he's very possessive about his nuns.

And we laugh and make our stand at Lumphanan in Mar.

See, I place the Boar's head here ... the men of Moray will form the shield ring ... you of Argyle stay out of it, I want you to harry their flanks ... but don't take any risks ... if we can't beat them tomorrow we simply retreat again ... it's a nuisance but I don't want any heroics ... we've got plenty of time ... this is our home ... whatever you may have heard, war is a sordid pastime ... it's not a game of shinty ... Give me a hunk of that bread, I'm starving.

In the dim dawn twilight Scotland stands shoulder to shoulder ... of course we are afraid, damn it, we are an imaginative civilised people ... but we know what we've got to do.

Then suddenly the bloody fog comes down.
I can't see a spear's length.
Is that you Dougal?
MacIan where are you?

Damn you, don't push, you'll have us all over! ... we are not advancing, but we are on the move ... I try to swing myself round to see what is happening behind me ... The safest feature of the shield wall is the worst feature of a shield wall ... what happens to one happens to all ... the back is moving so we have to move ... that or have them walk through us ... I shout an order to advance ... there's nothing I can do but go with it ... we right ourselves ... the good land that is Scotland is solid again under our feet ... we are through their front rank ... they pour off us like water ... we are invincible ... and then, oh my God, somebody has slipped ... ay, and at last the patience I have kept for twenty-three years breaks ... oh Finn, how could you give this up? ... This for Thorfinn ... that for Gruoch ... and this for what you would do to us ... you grasping, ignorant, illiterate bastards!

Sings

        Faces of greed, swords cruel and keen,
        There at Lumphanan surrounded the High King,
        Blithely the wall broke then ceaseless the swording,
        Spear unto spear spoke, bloody and blurred:
        Accept of our life's blood and we have rewarding.
        Screams high the battle bird,
        Reddened men's hands in blood.

and twelve hundred years are swept away.

> Humbled the homesteads
> Burning in Scotland.
> Red flame from smoking thatch
> Shoots high: for that day
> Dire danger failed not!
> Slain was the Ard Righ
> By the young lord.

No ... not quite the end ... but don't worry, not long now ... they'll still be serving ... but there's a wee twist I think you might enjoy ... oh yes, in a way I win ... my followers get my body away ... and to Malcolm's annoyance it is taken to Iona ... St. Colme's Inch ... the Isle of Kings ... and they give it a royal burial ... ay, and he isn't even able to capture Scone, not before my stepson Lulach has been elected Ard Righ ... The Englishman is not King yet ... But it was a foolish resistance ... twenty-three years of peace is not the best preparation for war ... within six months every major stronghold is in Malcolm's hands.

Lulach is invited to a peace conference.
Of course he went.

Under Celtic law hospitality is a sacred trust, the shame of Glencoe is not that a few thieving caterans were sent prematurely to their maker, but the way in which they were sent.

But Malcolm has been brought up in England ... Yes, Lulach was dirked in his bed by the very man who should 'against his murderer shut the door, not bear the knife himself.'

Ah well, that's death, eh? ... but Lulach too rests in Iona ... we're not far away from each other ... not that he's in any danger now ... because you see, Malcolm and his descendants are not here, are they?

Oh no ... they were refused burial here ... of course they were ... they are not true Ard Righ n'h'Alba ... Where's the Lia Fail?

For God's sake you don't really believe that bit of Perthshire sandstone Robert the Bruce used to fool the English is the real thing do you? The Lia Fail came from Ireland, surely you know that? ... That lump of rock you're all gawping at in Edinburgh Castle might just have well remained where it was. It's a fake. Yes, they lost it and there's no place for people who can lose things like the Fia Fail on Iona, they have to make do with plots in that fine new minster Saint Margaret built on stolen ground at Dunfermline.

Rest in peace ... if you can.

Remember what I said about disappoint a tradition and nothing is left but fear and superstition.

Holds up a copy of the play

Which is the true tradition?
This? ...

Pointing to himself

... or this?
Are you still afraid of me? Or will you have a stone now?
Bona dies et pax vobiscum.

Blackout and Bow

A Woman of Some Importance

In this play I dispense with the convention of having my character
start by retelling her life in old age and and slip back to the past.
The action is all a reliving.

Edith Nesbit: Stop it Harry! ... Let go of my hair ... please!
People are looking at us.

Oh what a very strange dream. All my life gone in the
twinkling of an eye ... then back to the beginning again.

Like a book.

Is all life just a dream or a series of dreams? If it is the problem
is going to be bringing the people we love from one dream to
another without the help of a magic carpet or an amulet or
something.

I'm not mad.

There really are a few people born now and then, like Francis
Bacon and Leonardo da Vinci, who are not bound by the rules of
time like the rest of us, and then, if the right bit of magic comes
their way, these people have the power to travel back and forth in
time just the way you and I go back and forth in space.

All you need is a ticket.

Our magic is someone else's normality, even if it sometimes
goes wrong and people get lost between worlds. Then people say
we're mad, but we're not, we're just displaced and terribly
confused.

Like our landlady's son at Halstead.

He lives all alone in a cottage at the edge of the village. Most
of the time he's quite normal and ever so polite but every six
months or so there's a knock at the front door and he's standing
there with a carpet bag.

"I'm afraid you've got to leave, Mrs. Nesbit, I'm the long lost
heir. I've come to take possession."

We invite him in. Mama gets him a cup of tea. Two sugars but
no milk.

23

"It is very clement for this time of year, isn't it, Joe?"

"Would you care for a piece of cake?" And then she asks him why he has come and he can't remember.

I'm terribly curious about what is in the bag. It's standing in the hall growling at me. Of course I open it, wouldn't you?

Three empty pickle bottles, a loaf of bread and a barrister's wig and gown.

And being a child I understand everything. It's simple isn't it? He's travelling, just like Harry and I do when we explore the Amazon.

Mama wouldn't understand. She got quite cross when I tried to explain I'd torn my dress going to Australia and she made us pay for a new nursery carpet from our pocket money when it got dirty on both sides going to France for the afternoon.

It's not nonsense. I don't know how to lie, yet. I'm not old enough, but adults know best so I'm having to think up stories she will believe, I am a very imaginative child.

But I mustn't forget, must I? I mustn't forget how last Thursday my bed suddenly sprouted wings and whisked us all back to France for an afternoon's tournamenting with King Arthur and his Court. It was great fun even though they haven't invented ice cream yet.

Mama is a dear. She's pretty and she's loving, and most frightfully good when you're ill, and always kind and almost always just, that is she is just when she understands things. No one understands everything, and mothers are not angels. She wants to do what is best for us, it's just that she doesn't always realise exactly what that is. I tried very hard to explain to her about France and the treasure and everything and she just lays down her pen and puts on a resigned expression.

"It sounds a lovely game darling, now please do be quiet I've got a lot of letters to write."

I burst into tears.

I don't know why they bothered to teach me to read before I went to school. It would have been much more useful if they'd taught me how to swop. There's a girl in my class, I call her Stewart Plaid, who's good at swopping. She always wears a tartan dress. I think her father's Scotch. I don't know why I agreed. I didn't want her silly old doll I want my dolls tea things. Mary gave them to me. Oh mummy I'm so unhappy.

And I'm to go to a different school, a boarding school. I think I'd have preferred a penal settlement, even a French one. My hair's always like this, and I'm told not to argue and sent to bed without my supper. I never seem to be good enough for supper. Mama should be given a reduction in fees.

Hurray, hurray, hurray Mary's not well. I'm sorry Mary I don't mean Hooray you're ill I'm just so happy that instead of going back to that dreadful school we're going to France.

Mary says I'm too young for France. I'm to be left luggaged with a French family while Mama looks for somewhere for us to live. They have a girl called Marguerite who's my age. She's the opposite to me and we're friends. I'm teaching her English games. She is trying her best but the French are so vain. I have two party dresses. My nice blue one and a brown thing Mama thinks I look nice in. Marguerite's only got one. It's grey. Isn't she a vain little girl? We've been invited out and she wants me to wear brown because my blue one shows hers up. So in her best interest I pretend I haven't heard her. Don't I look smart? and I fall over backwards into a tub of dirty dishwater. Stop laughing. Stop laughing or I'll hit you ... and I'm sent to bed again while Marguerite goes to the party in my brown dress because her grey one got torn in the scuffle ... but I do like her and we are going to keep in touch for ever and ever.

It's not fair is it? You spend every day for two months playing with somebody, sharing sweets and secrets and having the most wonderful adventures, then these people with whom you've fought side by side against King John's barons, Attila the Hun and Napoleon's Grenadiers, quite an achievement that, getting a French person to fight against Napoleon, just move out of your life and never come back.

But we're a family again, and I think perhaps Mary's going to go away too. That's why we're doing all the things she wants to do. It's so important everything is nice for her. Today we're going to have an expedition. We've hired a large open carriage and we can all stretch out and take our shoes off. Why are we stopping? The driver says his stepson is joining us. No he isn't says Mama, but he does and we put our shoes on. Oh no not more relations. His brother in law and his wife ... and two cousins, some friends of theirs, a large dog and two very fat ladies. I hate the French, they've spoiled Mary's outing.

We're back in England for the summer. France is too hot for Mary. Mama lets us run wild as long as we turn up for meals with hands and faces moderately clean; except of course when visitors are expected, then we are seized, scrubbed, clothed and made to look like the good children we certainly are not. But most of the time we have our own way. We are able to explore the Nile right to its source. We found it long before Doctor Livingstone and with half the trouble. Well Harry found it actually.

I'm so much better at holidays. I run away from two schools and just when I've found one I really like with lots of dear nuns who call me their "Bon petit diable" Mama is asked to take me away because there are too many empty wine bottles among my things.

I think one of the awfulest things about being at a boarding school is that you are never able to be on your own. You do lessons with people. You eat with people. You sleep in a dormitory ... and if you wander off sooner or later someone always comes along to see what you are up to.

Well now for the very first time in my life I have a real room of my own, even if it is rather a small room. Here I can dream and write poetry. No you can't see it Harry. Mummy, Harry and Alfred have been in my room. I know they have. I left a hair across the front of the drawer. See it's gone. Mama tells me not to be silly but I think its very sensible for someone who writes poetry, even someone who is going to be acknowledged as a great poetess, like Sappho, well not like Sappho exactly, but you know what I mean, to keep her work away from her elder brothers. That was probably the start of Sappho's troubles, she let her brothers read her poetry.

My room's got a trapdoor into a passage under the roof which runs all round the house. There's no floor and you have to step very carefully from rafter to rafter. In between it's just plaster and I'd fall through the ceiling of the room below. It's my secret place between worlds and times. I wish I'd a trunk with different costumes in it. I'm sure if I fell through in the right costume I'd be back in the time of the clothes.

Mary is so much better. She's engaged to the blind poet Philip Marston, who's a member of the Pre-Raphaelite Brotherhood and a friend of Mr. Swinburne, who patted me on the head last week and called me a pretty child, and if that doesn't impress you what about Dante Gabriel Rossetti kissing me during a game of hide and seek? I feel very encouraged and grown up I can tell you. Well most of the time. I do have my occasional relapses, like the evening we went to hear the band and see the illuminations of the thanksgiving for the recovery of the Prince of Wales and I allowed Harry to persuade me to throw a cracker into the mouth of the trombone. You should have seen the poor man's face.

Mary has had a relapse.

I am to be sent into exile in Islington. I don't even have a mouse to share my meals with. It's such a dreary little square. There isn't a garden, not a real garden, everyone is awesomely respectable and the house is terribly tidy as if no-one really lives here. It is furnished in sterile good taste that has been acquired from magazines and is terribly conscious of other people's opinion. Of course there are no books, books collect dust. Well there is a Bible and a few bound volumes of "Good Words" but that's it. My host is a doctor, we never see him, except at meals, his wife means to be kind but she's so obsessed with the Court Circular and what the neighbours say, any warmth she may have once had went out years ago. Everybody says she's so kind I feel guilty not loving her. She's bored that's the trouble. They are a terrible advertisement for marriage. They never fight and they don't seem to notice how unhappy they are. I wonder if they still ... you know? They share a room. Well at my age these things are the sort of things you've just begun thinking about. Well I have.

Isn't boredom catching? It's worse than the smallpox and there's certainly an epidemic in this house, even if the doctor hasn't noticed.

Yes I'm terribly silly but I'm desperate.

Everyone is in bed. I creep down to the surgery. It's freezing in here. I put my candle on the table. I can't stop shivering. All the medicines are in green bottles. I thought that meant poison, waiting to be wrapped up and labelled. I get a large jug from a shelf and pour the lot, yes, every bottle, into it. Then I mix them all together in a grand pharmaceutical cocktail, refill the bottles, and go back to bed.

I don't know why I did it. Yes I do, nobody seems to notice me ... and they still don't. No, nothing happened. Presumably all the patients took my medicine but nothing happened. Well some got better and some didn't, but nobody noticed. Then his wife opens my letter to Harry. I know she'd no right but she did all the same.

"It was very irresponsible of you Edith, somebody could have died."

I am sent home in disgrace.

Mama doesn't seem to notice. Yes Mary is dying. I have a wonderful last three months with her. It's so unfair, she's so young.

And then I suppose I grew up. I've even plucked up the courage to show Mama one of my poems. She thinks it good enough to send up to "Good Words", and has written a covering letter. I've added a P. S. "Do please take this."

London is a horrid place.

Let's go back to Halstead, but London is home now.

I think I've just become engaged to a Mr. Stuart Smith. He works in a bank. Yes, Mama we're going to Hyde Park. No, we won't be on our own he's bringing a friend to chaperone us. A Mr. Hubert Bland, who's a Socialist. They work in the same bank. Don't you trust me? I'm a grown up woman.

Isn't Mr. Bland a scream? he mixes up words. We're having some tea and instead of ordering chocolate chip cookies, he asks for chikky chocky poopies. The poor waitress is very confused. I feel ever so guilty but Mr. Smith is so old, and he never says he loves me, though I say it all the time. I know, I know, I know, but I need to hear you say it, Stuart.

Come back Mr. Smith. You can't just walk out of my life like this. Let's keep in touch shall we? I don't want to love my friend.

Oh Hubert why does he have to be so bitter? If only he'd said he loved me and given me hugs like you do. I need hugs.

Hubert is so sensitive and so funny, except when he's being serious. He really cares, no I don't mean about me, silly, or his friends ... about everything ... about Society. I've never thought about things like this before. Don't you see Mummy we really must give Cook every Sunday off. It's her right.

Stuart and I never quarrelled, well not till the end. That was the trouble I got bored with you. Hubert and I fight all the time. He calls me a silly spoiled intellectually arrogant bourgoise parasite and I get very cross with him because of course I am, aren't I? ... and he puts his arm round me and starts licking my lips.

I am sent to Manchester to stay with my Aunt. What's wrong with Hubert? he's quite well off. After we're married he's going to leave the bank and invest all his money in a brush factory. We are all dependent on brushes. Everything from teeth to chimneys needs a brush. The brush is a fundamental necessity of modern civilisation, and my Hubert has the vision to appreciate their significance.

Before they sent me to Australia, I mean Manchester, I was seeing Hubert every day but now I'm not seeing him he's with me every night. We write every day. Well I write to him every day. Sometimes he's too busy. Mama is normally so wise but she doesn't seem to appreciate the intimacy of the written word. I can talk to somebody for simply hours and hours and hours and never really progress much beyond mild flirtation, but if someone's written something for me, that's when I get to know them really well.

Do you think that's why one's best friends are often one's favourite novelists and why it's so sad when someone tells you they're dead? Except that no one who writes books can ever be absolutely and completely dead until everybody stops reading them.

... But these letters are private — Just for me and mine for him. Vicious and long winded expositions of our one sided views on every conceivable subject of non interest to humanity. They are our affair.

Oh Mama, Mama, Mama, thank you, thank you, thank you. You did know best after all. If I hadn't been banished to the salt mines of Manchester none of these would have ever have been written and I wouldn't be able to read them over and over again like this. "Thee I choose, all I refuse" isn't that a beautiful thing to say? "All my love, Hubert."

He comes up most weekends. There's a very good train service. Today he's allowed me to persuade him to take me back to Halstead. The Hall is all shut up and we aren't able to get in. Let's explore the woods. I catch a chaffinch and we kiss it and each other. I'm starving, what on earth's the time? What do you mean your watch has stopped? You know what I'm like if I don't have any lunch. I'm Hungry Hubert ... and he suggest we just knock on someone's door and hope they'll take pity on us. She does. Although she's a little disapproving at first and brushes the back of my dress in a most disapproving manner before giving us directions for the railway station. Oh is that what she thought we'd been doing? Surely I'd have taken it off, and we laugh and hug and treat ourselves to a Handsome and Hubert dares me to take the reins and drive it standing on the roof ... but I don't in case people think I'm fast or that we are a fire engine or something.

He wouldn't have liked me to really. He can be very conventional even though he is a Socialist.

I'm going to have to get used to being Mrs. Edith Bland. Oh yes, that's who I am now. Haven't I introduced myself? Mrs. Edith Bland, since eleven o'clock this morning. Yes we eloped. What was the point of waiting any longer? It would just have meant the farmer's wife was right after all. Mama is far too sensible not to like him now we're married. Please don't cry, I do love him very much, and she says it's not that she doesn't like him it's that she doesn't trust him, which isn't the same thing at all.

Yes we went to a registry office in the City. We thought all you needed was a license. Hubert had to dash out into the street and kidnap a friendly cabby and a fat man in a frock coat who gave me a sovereign to buy a wedding present, only Hubert gave it to the cabby for his trouble. I wish you'd been there, I forgot father's first name and the registrar got terribly cross with me.

Lewisham's ever so cheap and Greenwich and Blackheath are only a walk away. Oh yes, Hubert has resigned from the bank, they gave him a lovely clock, yes, that one. He's a brush manufacturer well he was till he caught smallpox and his partner absconded with all our brush factory money leaving us absolutely penniless. There's no need to look like that Mama. No, I don't need help. I can write, I can paint ... a bit ... and yes I can recite poetry at working men's concerts ... yes my own poetry. No I'm not going to recite now, I only recite for money. People say they're jolly well written. I've always had a good memory for the unusual phrase, people admire my manipulation of words, moving you all with quite conventional poetic patterns then stamping on them harder than Harry accidentally stamped on my new coral necklace with Raggetts Really Reliable School Boots. I'm renowned for the unusual, perhaps an unexpected colloquialism, perhaps something archaic or humorous. If you want to know what I'm talking about read next months "Sylvia's Home Journal". I think Hubert's illness and the brush factory going bust are positively the best set of misfortunes that ever happened to anybody, without them I'd never have started writing this, and I'd definitely never have plucked up the courage to put my poems and short stories in a shopping bag and go round banging on editors' doors.

Here am I, heavily pregnant, drinking cocoa out of the only cup and sitting in her office chair, while dear Alice Hoatson "Home Journal's" reader, contents herself with a milk jug on the floor. Dear Alice, she likes my work so much I can give up reciting. Yes, I know I liked it at first but it was becoming a bore.

The Bland finances are completely restored. Iris is a very healthy baby and Alice has moved in with us. We've even got a servant, well we had a servant until last week. She was supposed to take Iris for a walk in the park, instead she went to visit a friend who was a smallpox carrier. Nothing happened to her or

Iris, but they brought the virus home with them. Hubert's in bed
again.

I must see this suit is sent to the cleaners, it would be the last
straw if he was to reinfect himself.

Finds a letter.

I shouldn't read it should I? but we all do.

Oh my God. Hubert how could you? And did you really have to
lie to the poor girl? Oh yes Alice he lied. She thinks he's a
bachelor and that they're engaged. She's got a ring and
everything. I bet he bought it with my money. He hasn't got any
of his own, has he? Of course it's not her fault. Hubert's a very
attractive man, surely even you can see that? Anyway she's
carrying, poor dear. Of course I went to see her. Well Hubert can't,
he'd give her smallpox. She's a dear and really fond of him. And I
suddenly remember Mr. Stuart Smith and we're both crying and
giving each other hugs. Hubert seduced her by licking her lips. I
can't remember the last time he seduced me. I need a lot of cuddles
first to be really seduced and somehow these days we never seem
to have the time. So I suppose it's my fault. You might sort out
anything Iris has grown out of. Oh don't look so disapproving, if
I want to befriend Hubert's woman, there's nothing noble about
it, I like Hubert's taste in women. After all I'm one of them
myself. I'm the one he married.

He's not so much unfaithful as naturally polygamous and there
are lots and lots of societies that are based on polygamy. It's a
socialist issue. It is. The Fabian Society had a meeting about it in
this house. Walt Whitman, the American poet was in the chair and
George Shaw defended it, to the great annoyance of Hubert's bête
noire Mrs. Emmeline Pankhurst, who wants all of us women to
have votes whether we want one or not.

She's got a lovely smile and can be quite beautiful when she
doesn't try, but as soon as she starts talking about Women's
Rights she looks sour as a lemon. That's why Hubert can't stand
her he likes his women to attract. Oh Emmeline, dear, don't you
ever listen to other people? Mr. Frazer explained it all: Men
invented religion because we were dominating them, only they
took it too far, as they always do. Yes, Alice she hates the truth,
that's why she goes to Church every Sunday. What a silly spoiled
creature she is. I think the right to a man is much more important
than access to government, but I didn't contribute. I suppose I am
for it in theory but sometimes I can't help getting very jealous

and that means I have to get together another parcel of Iris's old things.

Oh yes, the Fabian Society always meets here and I only very occasionally have to resort to a fainting fit or something in order to attract attention. When I do Hubert gets terribly angry. Please don't give me away. I promise I won't smoke for at least a week if you don't, not even with a holder. Yes, Alice I don't need his permission, can't you see that's why I'm supporting us all at the moment, yes one poem, an article and a short story for Sunday dinner per week. That's a great many words I can tell you. Thank goodness all our friends are supplying me with plots. Ssh, I can't write with all this racket, ssh!

I've got a real book coming out at last. Hubert's going to give me a bracelet as a prize. I'm to have a bracelet for every book I write. I'm going to have bracelets from here to here, like one of those African ladies whose place in the household is measured by the number they have. We've got to send copies to simply everybody. What do you think, should I sign them all? If I do any more it's the ones that aren't signed that will be valuable. Did you read this? Mr. Haggard thinks that for once my politics enhance rather than mar.

I should be utterly exhausted, shouldn't I? I'm not. Work gives me the energy to do more work. When I'm writing a lot I can always find the time to wash my hair, turn sheets, cook the dinner and tell bedtime stories, things that are very hard work when I'm not.

You should do some exercises too, Hubert, anyone would thing you were pregnant. There isn't something you haven't told me, is there? Well then, I'll lend you my skipping rope. No, silly, you'll do yourself an injury, you've got to work up to things gradually. Isn't it funny, Iris and Paul are much more impressed by the fact that their mama can do high kicks than that she writes books and things. I think its because everybody we know is a writer, they think it's a very ordinary thing to do.

Hubert has brought me one of these new tricycles with solid tyres and a basket to put things in ... please come and see it, well what shall we call her? Of course it's a woman, it's useful ... but I'm not to take her on holiday ... I'm not to take anything. The Spring cleaning is finished and we are ready for the new year. Alice is coming too. She's not been very well. She's sick every morning. She's sick every morning.

Hubert how could you? She is my best friend. Stop lying to

me. Leave me alone. No Hubert it is too late ... and he starts to lick my lips. Of course I'm not going away. You need me. Alice needs me, she's my best friend. If anyone should leave it's you. Oh Hubert, push, push, oh!

When it's born I'm going to adopt it. At least Alice keeps him at home, and she's becoming quite good at turning sheets, though I wouldn't trust her to cook dinner for us ... yet. I just hope we don't get any missionaries. It's simply appalling what they've done to the poor Africans. It was a wonderful system: every time the man took a new woman the head wife got extra help around the Kraal, the more lecherous the man the more help for wife number one. — and then our missionaries come along and said one man one wife and the poor sillies got rid of all the really useful women and kept the youngest and least experienced, then all their tribes fell apart and they had to become part of the British Empire. Luckily we don't get many missionaries in South London.

Well, except Alice and I! We are holding a party this year for the Deptford poor children. There will be games, food and entertainment which I'm going to write for them.

I've really begun something with these entertainments, haven't I? Pantomime for children without the boring traditional bits like the Harlequinade. I know Mr. Shaw says they are not pantomimes, his plays aren't tragedies, well Hubert says they're not. I don't think it matters what something is, if it's fun. That's what mine are, funs.

Bills, bills, bills. Please Mr. Butcher can't you see we must keep faith with the children? I just don't have the time to write stories to pay you and do all this. Have you done the decorations Alice? Oh and Iris, Humpty's costume needs cleaning, see to it for me will you.

There are over one thousand children to be catered for this year. I know we've got to find somewhere bigger. Help Herbert, we can't disappoint a thousand children. Thank you Mr. Wells, the Governors are quite happy to lend us Deptford School. Yes your letter made all the difference.

Now everything's grown like this it's not nearly so much fun. I like to do everything myself. I hate committees ... and sub-committeees. I think the worst thing is having to arrange rotas. I'd got the whole afternoon organised. I was going to write. Alice has taken the children out to give me some peace. Knock, knock, knock. I'm not going to answer it. I've a poem to finish for tomorrow. Knock, knock, knock. Oh for God's sake what do you want?

"Mrs. Blank won't be able to sit in the hall this afternoon."

Oh well, no poem, no Sunday roast.

What's so terribly unfair is she won't do any stint in exchange. She's jealous of me because my stall always does better than hers at the bazaar. But I mustn't crow, must I? We must learn to forgive our enemies, even when they try to claim that the box of Benares brass and Indian souvenirs which I accidentally left behind her stall was hers. Do you know she actually stood on my hand when I was reaching to get it. It really hurt and she got very angry indeed. Have you noticed how when people hurt other people it's the one who does the hurting who gets angriest and when they do say they are sorry they make it sound as if they are doing you a huge favour.

The Fabian Society is growing too big as well. It was much more fun when the meetings were all held here. I can't be bothered with it these days. Surprise, surprise, Hubert and I agree about something. So we've started our own debating society called "It". Mr. Frazer, or rather Sir James, he's been K'd, which we're all rather thrilled about, well all except Hubert who says it isn't very Socialist, I think you're jealous, gave the first talk on the marriage customs of Indian and Burmese tribes. I thought it was going to be boring too, but it wasn't. Emmeline got very very angry and tried to argue that there must be women in India who had some sort of secret society. Sir James said yes there was they were called prostitutes and she stormed out in a huff.

But much more my kind of evening was when Lawrence Housman dressed up as a baby and Alfred Suttro defended him for breach of promise. He's only allowed to use baby talk.

"Aggedy- daggedo do ... weeby beeby, puba" that kind of thing, but it always means something different. It does. Iris only had one word for six months ... "dis" ... "What do you want?" ... "Dis" ... "Who's your papa?" "Dis" ... "What's your name?" "Dis" ... Hubert used to call her Dissy but it didn't stick. Anyway Alfred interprets everything so seriously that we're all ill from laughing and then George Shaw sums up, he's the judge telling us all that marriage is the poison of romance and that of all forms of the passion of love from the possibly platonic to the blisterously illegal, the connubial is least adapted to it.

I read my latest story. This is much more fun than your silly old Fabians. Why does somebody have to spoil things for everyone else. A very silly young man who shall remain nameless, gave us a rather different talk on nudity illustrated by lantern slides of women lying on tiger skin rugs which Hubert said was in the worst of taste. Poor Aubrey I don't think he meant to upset everybody. But Hubert says we're not going to have any more meetings.

Anyway, we really must do something to save money. I seem to be writing a lot more for children these days. It's not deliberate. I've run out of ideas again and Alice suggests I try writing up the children's bed-time stories. They're all our old favourites brought up to date. You know, out of work Kings signing on at the Labour Exchange, princesses being spoiled and bad tempered like you, Iris. The Strand simply love them, so our finances have recovered a little. I've bought Hubert a new smoking jacket because I've got an idea.

I should be very angry, shouldn't I? If I'm to be a good mother. It's not funny and Paul asks me why I am laughing, and I give him a hug because he was only trying to make a contribution to the book-keeping by waylaying old gentlemen on their way home from the city and begging for pennies. He'd collected three and six so it wasn't such a stupid idea. I'm going to call it "The Story of the Treasure Seekers" and it will unfold the saga of the six Bastable children's attempts to recover their family fortunes. The narrator Oswald is my finest creation. You see the trouble with telling a story in the first person is how to strike the right note for describing heroic deeds in which the hero has participated. Most people, probably because they haven't done enough heroic deeds themselves, can't do this. Mock modest just makes me squirm. Oswald is honestly admiring of his own ability. He's every right to be so. Whenever I do a noble action or am particularly clever I damn well make sure everyone knows about it. There'd be no point in doing any noble actions if I didn't, would there?

Treasure hunting with the Bastables has certainly paid for itself. The Strand is so scared I'll take them elsewhere that they've raised my fee to thirty pounds a story ... yes, the same rate as Mr. Doyle gets for Sherlock Holmes and Doctor Watson and they are guaranteeing that each dozen or so will be grouped together and republished in book form.

Our finances haven't just recovered they are better than they've ever been. New boots for everyone and a goose for Sunday dinner.

Well what do you think children. Yes this is our home now. Well House, it reminds me of Halstead. I feel better already I've always been a country person. Oh don't be silly Paul, there's a lot more to do here than in London. You can explore the Nile for a start, and dig for treasure, and if you do run out of things I'm sure the nursery carpet can take you to France, and they look at me the way Mama used to. Children who've been brought up in a city have no imagination.

I'm going to stay here for twenty years at least and write ever so many books. I'll start as soon as we've got everything unpacked. Oh doesn't everything smell nice. You know what it smells of don't you? Childhood, those marvellous exhilarating summers of childhood.

Don't say I'm stupid. I'm quite aware of all the drawbacks. We haven't got enough furniture, we're miles and miles from all our friends and it is impossible to keep servants ... but we've got a ghost, and not just any old ghost. Sir Thomas More no less. Well just his head actually. I'm glad it's not just the body, how would be recognise him? and Hubert makes a very rude suggestion. It's not that funny Alice anyway I'm sure he was far too nice a person to display himself like that with children in the house. What happened was that after his friend King Henry cut his head off, as a sort of practice for cutting off the heads of his wives later on, Sir Thomas's daughter brought it here and buried it in the garden. You see, children, I said there was a treasure. I'm sure the Archbishop of Canterbury or somebody would pay a great deal of money for the head of Sir Thomas More.

Don't be silly it's what makes the house interesting. But servants see things differently and refuse to live in. We can manage. A lady from the village comes up and does for us every day. She's a very good worker, but I'm afraid I'm letting her go she can fit far too much into that bucket of hers. Tea and butter I'm prepared to turn a blind eye to, Sunday's joint is the last straw. So I'm afraid you'll have to peel the potatoes Alice, I've got to get this finished for tomorrow's post.

We have completely furnished one room with all our very favourite things, like my roll top desk, Hubert's mother's grandfather clock and the Second Empire chaise longue Harry and Alfred gave us for a wedding present. Obviously Sir Thomas has been giving us a chance to settle in, which is after all the kind of consideration you'd expect from a man like him. Well a ghost like him.

Until last night.

I am woken by a sound which can only be the sound of blood

dripping from his neck. Plop ... plop ... plip ... plippity plop. It is coming from our room. Hubert tells me not to be silly and arms himself with an umbrella, our best steel fire-irons have been missing since we moved ... and in the best Oswald Barstable manner cautiously opens the door.

Isn't it lucky he's got an umbrella? Water is simply pouring through a hole in the ceiling, plaster everywhere. The children have woken up by this time and I haven't the heart to send them back to bed. I do try but they're having such a wonderful time. We all are. Hubert and Paul are on the roof trying to unblock drains by torchlight and getting in each other's way. Alice, Iris, Fabian and Rosamund are carting everything out mopping up. You can't move in the hall but the fire-irons have turned up. Fabian had put them in the clock. It's five o'clock before we get back to bed. Of course we have cocoa, you have to have cocoa when you have a flood, it's obligatory, and Hubert is very loving. Yes we christened the house. I'm so happy.

Even the plumber's bill can't spoil things. Four pounds, sixteen shillings and seven pence, that's five pages of Oswald. The next day the man from the water company comes to inspect the work and makes us install new taps, another eight pounds. Yes almost half a story. It doesn't matter Hubert, it won't take me long ... and it doesn't. The flood makes a wonderful chapter and we're having a simply marvellous time chopping wood, putting up shelves, cleaning boots, sweeping, scrubbing and cooking. Work is what you hate doing and have to do for a living, not that I hate writing but you know what I mean. There are times when you just don't feel like doing it and it's a real effort remembering what you've decided that your characters can do and can't, and they're not making things any easier by just remaining in the ink bottle, instead of helping out. That's work. Everything else is play. Come and hold this for me Iris, please, and hand me another screw.

I'm so happy. I'm not even jealous that Hubert has christened the house with Alice as well. We're all eighteen again and very much in love. It's so wonderful to be back in the country again after all these years. Poor Hubert he's having to do all the work, and serve him right, I'm pregnant again and so is Alice. You'd think he'd have more sense than to put us both out of action at the same time? Men don't think do they?

Why do Alice's children live and mine have to die? I'm forty one and I can't have any more, she can. The doctor says I smoke too much and that I should get a new writing chair. If I don't smoke there aren't any stories and this is the chair I've always written in. Damn this headache. Do you ever get headaches on the side of your nose Alice? No it's not a cold, it's a headache I know the difference. I wish you could finish this story for me.

I wake up at four o'clock every night with indigestion. I'm drinking pints of this stuff. Yes, bicarbonate of soda, and other things. It kills the pain. There is no pain. It's all in my mind. I'm never ill. I can't be, not with Hubert, Alice and the children to look after.

Well you are all going to have to look after yourselves. The doctor has confirmed it. I've got cancer.

Of course I'm frightened. Nobody wants to die. It's such a waste. I still haven't written my best book.

Experts can be wrong.

I've not got cancer, but Fabian is to have a minor operation at home. No nothing serious or they'd have him into hospital. He'll be down for lunch directly he comes round from the anaesthetic. Of course he's going to come round, it's only a minor operation. Let me go to him. I'm his mother let me in. No ... No ... No. He's just cold. I'll warm him. Get some hot water bottles. Alice I order you to get me some hot water bottles. Quickly! Hurry!

It's no good, is it? My children die. Alice's are all right but mine die. If only I could go back to the past. Only if I should it wouldn't be the past, would it? It would be now. I could be with Fabian and Harry and Mother and Hubert all at the same time.

Only Hubert would get bored and go to his room. I don't know why people bother coming to visit us. But they do, don't they? They call the Friday night six o'clock from Canon Street, the Well House train. If it is late we just go to bed leaving a notice telling first timers the front door is at the back. That's not as silly as it sounds. Our official Front Door opens directly into the hall and the house gets terribly cold if the door is constantly being opened. So we keep it shut. I love visitors but I'm getting too old to allow them to interfere with my comfort. It's important that I finish my chapter before I come down. No chapter ... no food. If you don't like the house rules you needn't come. But they do don't they? I am the first down, Alice knows better than to dare appear before me. Hubert is the last to appear. What? Oh for God's sake people don't come to Well House they come to see me.

They call me the Duchess. Does that mean they think I'm getting old. People aren't buying as many books these days. Still there's only me now isn't there, after Hubert died Alice moved out and Iris is in Paris studying art. It's funny to think of Iris grown up and Fabian still a child. I went to see her. We met a dreadful old drunk who came staggering up to our table when we were having coffee on the Boulevard ... oh I can't remember the name, just up from the Place de la Concorde. Do you know he was an Englishman who'd set some of my poems to music thirty years ago. He insisted on performing them for us on the café piano. Yes badly out of tune. I was terribly embarrassed but Iris thought it was rather sweet. She's a funny girl.

They say children have stopped reading my books. So I'm writing an adult novel based on student life in Paris. Of course I'm in it, as Iris, there's so much of me in that child. So are all her friends.

Well I think it's a very good book and you must have thought so too or you wouldn't have published it. If you don't want to publish another I'll just have to take lodgers. It was Skipper's idea really. Skipper Tucker, my husband.

Haven't I introduced myself? I'm Mrs. Tucker now. Of course he can't replace Herbert, I can't replace his Sophy who was very quiet and patient unlike me. But I can talk to him about Hubert and he can talk to me about Sophy and that's a help. Skipper's one of those people with a compulsion to help.

I really do appreciate the things he does around the house. I wouldn't let him do them otherwise. I could do them myself, of course I could. I'd do them a little differently but I'd do them. Skipper knows all about having the right tools and measuring things. He gets very impatient with my "knock another nail in" philosophy. He likes things to be done properly which is why I didn't marry him right off.

We are having a cup of tea and I'd spilt the sugar lumps and he's down on his hands and knees picking it up, he doesn't even have a jacket on and he has his back to me, well, not his back exactly! ... and he just says "Looks as though you need a tug around here" He's very nautical that's why we call him Skipper.

Now I may be a little unconventional, advanced even, and I may not be in the first blush of womanhood but I do not think it is unreasonable to expect a man who wants to marry me to put on his jacket and look me in the eye when he proposes. I'm not demanding a sheaf of sonnets and three dozen red roses, I'm even prepared to overlook the fact that he doesn't go down on one knee and say "By my Halidame fair lady I would be your faithful knight," but sticking a rear end in my face, festooned with yellow braces and calling me, by implication, an old cargo boat ... I need a tug, forsooth! It's too much. I like things properly done too. So I keep him waiting, but he is such a useful man, so very practical and so very stubborn.

Of course paying guests aren't the same as the real thing but it's nice to have people about the house again, and I suppose we need the money. The man at Macmillans says the post war generation of children don't want my books any more, that they're old fashioned. He's quite wrong. What it is is that people are not buying them, like me they haven't any money, so they're borrowing other people's copies, and that of course means not as many are being sold, but surely a new book, that they couldn't borrow, would be quite another basket of fish. I've got an idea about a magic wardrobe from which people can get into another world that's going on not quite parallel to this one ... there were going to be all sorts of people in this world, old friends like giants and talking beasts and things and new people who don't exist yet because I haven't been allowed to create them ... or do they?

If anyone starts talking to you about Marsh Wiggles and Dufflepuds you'll know they've got to my world ... only the man at Macmillans says it's a silly idea and that nowadays children want books about real things.

It's so nice being able to talk to Skipper about Hubert. We had such a good time, but there is no such thing as time, is there? Time can only be measured by heart beats, everything happens so quickly.

Fade to Black

Hello, Juno Speaking

an entertainment

I see this piece as an experiment in merging the techniques of stand up comedy and the one person play. It should be seen as a flexible entertainment rather than a formal play. Juno's office should reflect her comments later in the script about churches. It is a mixture of workplace and home. She is being interviewed by a naive young female journalist.

Juno: What's this to be about then? Juno casting, my murky past, or the book?

I see "it's up to me". That means you want all the dirt, doesn't it? Nothing changes.

Of course you can take photographs, darling. Where would you like me? How about over here by the window looking out wistfully at everything I've lost? "Wist" is one of my strong suits. I was Goddess of "wist" once.

No? ... at my desk writing the sequel, or I could be signing a copy to you. I expect you to give me a good plug.

No! I do not do that kind of pose at my age.

Interviewer compliments her on her appearance.

Thank you very much ... Six thousand and two next birthday ... honestly ... well that's what this book's about, isn't it? How to reduce without eating brown rice, "Mind over fatter." ... No, I'm not exactly Junoesque any more, am I? Poor Rubens he'd be so disappointed, he had such a passion for vast expanses of pink flesh, but you have to move with the times, don't you? If you are not a size twelve, and a Miss Selfridge size twelve at that, people start suggesting you should go to aerobics. The secret is to look as if you go to aerobics... oh yes, if you are a casting director glamour is very important. Actresses can be so Oxfam, can't they? It's up to us casting directors to bring a little style to the business. But no, if you want that kind of pose it's my daughter Aphrodite you should be interviewing.

Oh, she's being done by "Cosmo" is she? Yes I can see she'd be right up their street. "Intimate Revelations." I shudder to think what she'll tell them. She can be very indiscreet.

She should never have married him, you know. A thousand years older if he was a day, obsessive about metalwork and of course being lame he didn't like dancing so they never went anywhere.

What? I'm sorry I keep forgetting you are not taught our family history any more, are you? It used to be the whole secret to understanding the English class system. Oh yes, if you knew about Greek and Roman mythology you were public school and upper class, the middle classes had a sound Christian education and could quote the Bible at you, while the working classes were encyclopaedic about cricket and football, well they were in Yorkshire, in the rest of the country it was just football. So reassuring. You could place people.

We're not giving anything away today are we? ... Let me guess, Cheltenham and Oxford? ... well I was right about Oxford. One of the men's colleges? ... thought so, one can sense your feminist tendencies, the men's colleges really bring that out. Perhaps if you had been to Cheltenham you'd have known about Deedee's marriage problems ... "Deedee" short for Aphrodite , that's what she called herself when she was a little girl, well god, you know what I mean. She couldn't say Aphrodite, Deedee, Deedee was the best she could do and it sort of stuck inside the family as a pet name, although she'd hate it if you called her that today. We're all to call her Venus now, which I've never thought suits her. Aphrodite's so much more ... well her ... isn't it?

Anyway she married her uncle Vulcan, well that's what the Romans called him ... I know it's very confusing of us to have so many names, isn't it? Makes you wonder what we're trying to hide. The tax people simply hate it. Vulcan? If I said he was a blacksmith it wouldn't really give you any idea of his importance, would it? Sounds very leather and working class, doesn't it? Hardly an occupation requiring cabinet responsibility, not under New Labour, but you see he made swords and things and having a better sword than your opponent was frightfully important. A sword that bent at the wrong moment could be most embarrassing for a man.

Yes, he was an arms dealer, thank you, that's a very good way of describing him. Obscenely rich, which I suppose some girls find very sexy, Deedee certainly did, but such a chip on his shoulder because my husband had made him suppress the cross bow. He was quite paranoid. Had a bodyguard. And he spent far too much time at the factory. You can't blame Deedee, young Mars was ever so pretty, we all had the hots for him. Face like a Greek god ... well yes, I know he was a Greek god, but then so was Vulcan. What you have to understand is that Mars was god of War which made him Vulcan's best customer. So he orders Deedee to be very nice to him ... and she was ... very.

Exactly you could say she was just carrying out her husband's orders. Oh yes, poor Vulcan was the last to find out. Mars's bar jokes had been going round Olympus for six months before he realised he was the joke.

I must say his reaction is a little heavy. He hangs a net over their bed, well his bed actually ... and drops it on them when they are in mid bonk. Then he summons a press conference.

Now that was a photocall.

The trouble was the scandal reflected on all of us. Worshippers like their gods to set an example. They'll forgive quite a lot if there are a couple of good harvests and they win their wars but this was pushing it. You see the only war that was going on when the story leaked was a no win situation for us. We were worshipped by both sides and with all the men in the armies there weren't any harvests. Most embarrassing. Everyone is blaming Deedee for interfering with Mars' training programme. There are rumours that he's missed squad sessions to be with her ... Exactly! a very good example, he was under the same sort of pressure as poor Will Carling was last year, everybody blamed his loss of form on his private life, and with pictures of them on every second urn he couldn't even deny it. It was that dreadful Homer person who broke the story. Nasty little man, always muck-raking and terribly biassed against Troy. He got it second hand in a bar. I never did find out who sold him the negatives. Mind you he got his come uppance didn't he? Oh yes, they sent him blind. Those pictures were strictly top shelf material. God sale only. But

Apollo was driving a new chariot a week later, Hydra skin covered seats so you can draw your own conclusions.

No, it's not an exact parallel. Deedee wasn't like her at all, no, much more like the other one ... Yes, that red-headed child you did that marvellous piece on about a year ago ... yes her ... They are both a bit Botticelli, aren't they? Rubens would simply have adored her ... yes, I should sell her a copy of the book shouldn't I? Only my method does require mind ... Deedee's debts were astronomical too, you know, my husband had to cancel her charge cards and issue a statement that Olympus wasn't taking any responsibility. Mind you she got a lot back from that book she did with the Indian chap, you know, the Karma something or other, there was even a pop-up version for children. Poor Deedee she never could resist a good looking young salesman.

Now that wasn't what I was implying at all, darling. As if I'd say things like that about my own daughter. But no, I know you are paying me rather well for this interview, but I have to think of my image. It wouldn't do to have the chief executive of Juno Casting on a casting couch, people feel threatened enough by us as it is. Anyway, I was a Queen once, even if it was a very long time ago.

Exactly, you can't predict the future, can you? ... oh no, Gods certainly can't. we're just as bad as you are, we're always trying to manipulate it, of course, but it's all a bit hit and miss ... yes, sometimes you'd think there was a curse on us or something. I lost a fortune on that silly war. I had Troy down for a home win and then their star striker Hector gets injured just before half time and the Greeks bring on Achilles as a super-sub. Even so if it hadn't been for that wooden horse we still might have won. I don't think it should have been allowed, very dangerous ... But you see if we could predict the future there wouldn't be any money in it, would there?

Oh yes it was our main source of income, we couldn't have made ends meet on sacrifice and donation. We each had our own speciality, mine wasn't very different to what I'm doing now ... yes, basically it was just casting. Finding the man or woman for the moment. I mean not every situation had the budget to afford Hercules or Helen of Troy. It was my idea to let Perseus do that Gorgon gig. There was a lot of resistance at first. My husband wanted Hercules of course, even though he was singlehandedly endangering more species than the fur trade, which meant he was losing popularity with young people. Perseus was a much better bet. It made him a star. Literally! That was one way of doing it. Apollo of course concentrated more on 'futures'. He ran a very lucrative scam at Delphi which all of us consulted from time to time. Not that it ever really helped. All it was was educated guesses based on current market trends, with a little speculative journalism thrown in ... and talking of speculative journalism, didn't I notice something in your February issue about Mr. Yeltsin giving serious consideration to the reinstatement of the Czar, you had a photograph of the young man outside the Imperial Palace at St Petersburg ... Well then I could be your chief goddess all over again, couldn't I? There's a lot of support for the idea of a female supreme being, particularly one with my business experience ... Exactly, we don't want questionable poses interfering with that little scenario, do we now?

Where shall we begin?

"At the beginning."

How predictable.

Oh no, it took a lot longer than seven days and your man didn't create it, darling. Oh dear no, where did you get that idea from? ... What! you don't want to believe that old codswallop. It's balls. So much translation and improvement it's quite unreliable. Worse than Homer, nothing even secondhand, well till the sequel, why there's even things about me in there, if you know where to look for them ... No, I'm not pointing them out for you, all the women are portrayed as harlots ... well apart from her, but that's a very dodgy story when you examine it ... yes. I used to renew my virginity at least once a year. It's quite simple if you know the right river.

But no, the world's much older than Him, and that's another thing I really object to. The way he's got us all conditioned to refer to him as Him with a capital H, or God, as if he was the only one. It's like someone with a PhD insisting on being called Doctor all the time, even when it isn't relevant. I mean you've probably got one, haven't you? ... I hope it isn't on your business card, that's so pretentiously insecure, it would put me off right away. Well it sort of tells me you preferred cotton wool to the real world for three years. No I'm afraid Jehovah wasn't around at the beginning to create anything, just bought the rest of us up when we were a bit down on our luck. I don't want to sound snobbish or anything but I always think of him as what you'd call New Money.

Oh darling, go to any of his temples, they're a giveaway. Nothing old and so designed, just that cross logo of his all over the place and expensive art. There isn't anything lying about to tell you people live there and what they're like. Even the song books are all neatly piled up at the end of the seats. No character. I remember attending a Christmas party at Saint Peters one year, with Pol, sorry Apollo. I don't mean to confuse you with all our names. No, of course we hadn't been invited just sneaked in with some American tourists, and he turns to me and says: "It's beautiful, isn't it? Right out of a magazine. The sort of place one comes home to and says, "well then where shall we go tonight?" Too formal, not lived in. Old Gods have little family heirlooms scattered about everywhere, you know, things that have been there forever and ever and forgotten about. I had bits and pieces in my temples from Thracia, Bithynia, Cappadocia, even Libya. Whenever we went anywhere, even if it was just for the day, we always brought something back ... Exactly, that's what made them home. I had ...

Phone rings

Excuse me, I'm sorry about this, could be important. We're casting a musical version of Hedda Gabler and Peter's such a ditherer. Can't make up his mind between Madonna and Emma Thompson.

Picks up phone

Hello, Juno Casting ... oh, it's you ... Look I'm in a meeting ... No darling, I can't talk to you now. I'll ring you back ... *(To interviewer)* How long will we be? ... *(To phone)* about half an hour ... and darling please don't ring mummy again, you know how she worries ... promise me now, and don't do anything stupid. ... yes, about half an hour ... Bye.

Puts phone down.

Sorry about that, my husband ... Where were we? Oh yes, temples. I'm very sentimental I'm afraid. My problem is I just can't bear to throw anything out. The attic is simply stuffed with cardboard boxes I still haven't got round to unpacking since I moved out of Olympus. They've been all round the world and never been out of attics. That's the trouble with possessions. It's nice to know you've got them, even if you don't quite know where they are. Somewhere there's a little black vase with a comic picture of me kicking my ex that I really treasure but I haven't a clue where it is except that it's in one of the boxes.

One of these days I really must do a car boot sale. I've got hundreds of sphinxes I'm sure someone could put to good use, not to mention shoes. I mean when we moved to Rome they were so cheap, I just couldn't resist them ... No, she'd nothing on me, I was an addict, a founder member of Boots Anonymous, but they are such marvellous things for throwing at partners and so much more environmentally friendly than thunderbolts. But that's all in the past now, isn't it? Nowadays because the rest of the profession is so disorganised I have to be extremely tidy and efficient. I sometimes think if I'd been more like I am now two thousand years ago we might still be running things ... yes I'm afraid we could be very arbitrary, rather like bad directors and just as arrogant.

Now that's a really brilliant idea, I have some very nice pieces Christies might be interested in. I've got a torso by Milo that's still got both its arms.

Nothing sentimental about Jehovah, I'm afraid. A good business man but a very jealous god. The last thing he wants people thinking about is his origins. Very dodgy! I could tell you a thing or two about them. Mind you he hasn't done badly for a provincial, has he? Started out with just a stall in Jerusalem market selling denim caftans and sandals to the locals, nothing over two shekels, and then about two thousand years ago took his son into the business and there was no stopping them, branches everywhere, well except Iran of course, that's always been a tough market. We had trouble there ourselves, went to war over it. Yes it was a marathon.

No that's not being fair. I know business may not be quite what it was for him in the fifteenth century. The firm's never been the same since that Luther person introduced trade unions ... yes you could say it's gone downmarket, certainly in the old days the Christmas sale wouldn't have gone on for quite as long and the service was more personal but it's still the only place to go if you want old fashioned religion. Its ritual is a real bargain. That's one of the things that did for us. Instant ritual was a brilliant idea.

When he offered to buy us out we didn't really have an option. It was more of a takeover really, especially of festivals and I was a tad sad that he changed all our old brand names, I mean Saturnalia sounds so much more jolly than Christmas, still he kept the mistletoe so I can't complain. I said to my husband ... you'd better use the Greek form for him, that's Z,E,U,S, Zeus, he never could abide being called Jupiter, or Jove, felt it was too familiar, and of course some people used to get confused between Jove and Jehovah which made him very angry, I said to him, if you must do business with a Jew make sure you keep a seat on the board, but he never had a good head for that sort of thing, used to spend all his time on his yacht with ... but I'm sure this is boring you, it's old gossip.

Didn't you know? Silly me, how could you, there's no chance of him ever making a comeback, not with his political views. If you'll excuse my language, basically they are "if you can't eat it or fuck it, zap it." ... He's just down the motorway, in a retirement home for the gods in Essex called Dundeifying. I think it's a Church of England charity. They all are. He has to share a room with that one-eyed northerner Odin ... yes him, very big here once, swapped his eye for the ability to see into me future ... Yes I know what I said about that, he was conned wasn't he? Having only one eye he couldn't see it clearly, so he was a lot worse off than he was before. It ruined his axe fighting. Made him vulnerable to an overhand right hook. That's why he lost his title and got bought out himself. Poor God all he's got now is a drink problem. So sad, one day you're ruling the universe, well in his case Yorkshire, the next you are being thrown out of the local pub for making indecent suggestions to the barmaid.

Oh we'd split up long before we were taken over. It was all very civilised. We both knew it wasn't working. Luckily there weren't any financial problems which made things easier. We'd independent cults. I'm a goddess in my own right you know, or I was then. If I'd had to rely on him I'd have starved, darling. I certainly didn't insist on half of Olympus, I hated the place. Very draughty, freezing in winter and simply no privacy. Once everyone had grown up it was far too big for us. He stayed on for another five thousand years or so. The girls looked after him, well Diana and Minerva did, Deedee had left of course and had a lovely little place on Cyprus. That's why they never got married, an overdeveloped sense of duty to dad. He had a real god's gift for making a girl feel guilty ... Yes, it's the one thing he has in common with Jehovah. But eventually even they'd had enough, it was impossible. I remember trying to help Diana choose a birthday present for him once. She was in a terrible state about it. I mean just what do you get the God who's got everything? Deedee used to get him silly things like white chocolate body rub, but Di wasn't that kind of girl. And he was always so ungrateful. "Do you like it dear?" "It's fine." Could mean anything. Why do the male sex find it so difficult to say thank you? I mean when they give us anything we're expected to be ever so impressed, aren't we? "How was it for you?"

And I'll tell you another thing, he'd simply no sense of prices. He expected them to manage on the same housekeeping money he was giving me when we first got married. If there weren't at least three courses on the table every night, whinge, whinge, whinge. And he never did the washing up, said it made his hands rough and he refused to wear rubber gloves. Men won't, will they? The price of sacrificial doves had rocketed in a couple of thousand years and an oven ready eagle was extortionate. They had to go round the supermarket every night at six o'clock looking for reduced to clear labels. It was so humiliating, everybody recognised them. They were subsidising him out of their own cults and all the time Olympus was falling down round their ears. Well no one would do any work for them on tick. He didn't believe in paying bills. It was against his religion. It was difficult enough trying to get away with that one during the Roman Empire when he was its official God and people could at least say By Appointment, but after he'd been taken over you couldn't even get someone to fix a tap.

Yes I'm afraid they just left him to it. You can't blame them. They weren't going anywhere. He was in a rut ... No, he missed his chance. Tried to get a job as a devil with the new lot but a classical education wasn't quite what they were looking for. I don't know, I think he changed his name and went to Australia. The aborigines have a legend about a chieftain's daughter who is sexually assaulted by a kangaroo that I've always thought very suspicious. Anyway I lost touch for a while then right out of the blue I get a card from the home saying he's given my name as a character reference. I can tell you I was very tempted but I didn't want him turning up on my doorstep with a sleeping bag. I'd just started this business and it could have been most embarrassing.

I visit every other Sunday and am terribly sympathetique.
Well you've got to allow a girl a bit of smug superiority, haven't
you? But he's let himself run to seed poor God. Not that he ever
did care much about shape. Bull, swan, even on one occasion an
aardvark, though Homer and Ovid seem to have missed that one.
No, I'm afraid his great pulling power was always just power, so
that when he lost the business and had to sell the yacht he was all
washed up, wasn't he? The things he says about Jehovah are
unrepeatable but what did he expect? Gods are always trashing
each other, sneaky behaviour is what Gods are all about, if
religion was simple there wouldn't be anything in it for gods in
the first place. It's not about Good and Evil is it? It's about
power. He didn't exactly pension off his father, did he?

I'm sorry, I'm forgetting your original question, aren't I? No,
in the Beginning, my great great grandmother, Euronyme, who
was Goddess of Everything then, and a very powerful lady, rose
naked from Chaos and didn't have anywhere to put her feet so he
created your world as a bathmat ... no I'm not making this up, it's
the only logical explanation when you think about it. A soft one,
not a rubber one. Mountains and valleys are just the way a
bathmat gets screwed up when you are drying yourself ... Exactly!
Now you are getting the idea, pools of water in some places, dry
bits at the edges ... of course it started off flat, all those people
falling off the edge are not just legends, poor old Odysseus was
absolutely terrified that was what he was going to do.

What happens to a bathmat after you've finished using it? ...
It gets bundled up into a ball and thrown in the dirty washing bag.
Well it does if you are female. If Euronyme had been a man it
would probably still be on the floor somewhere and the flat
earthists would be right, but she wasn't and that's what happened
to this world. Euronyme bundled it up, stuffed it in her bag and
forgot about it for millions and millions of years. It just lay there
growing things and getting very smelly. Oh yes, leave
something at the bottom of a dirty washing bag and all sorts of
universes are the result. There's a whole Y-front dimension but
none of the planets have a breathable atmosphere so the life
forms are too strange even for Star Trek the Next Generation. No,
not the sort of thing for your readers they are going to find it hard
enough accepting that their world is just a bath mat for gods to
wipe their feet on as it is.

Yes it was a complete accident. You weren't chosen or

anything, what a delightfully arrogant idea. No it damned nearly stayed in the washpile and of course if it had you'd never have progressed beyond dinosaurs. What finally wiped them out was mummy hiding a baby in it.

You don't know about this either do you? ... Don't apologise I'm sure you are far more computer literate than I am, but it's quite a story. Daddy was dreadfully superstitious. Planned his whole life round the number of magpies he saw and his horoscope. Mummy used to check all the papers everyday to make sure he got a good one. They can be so irresponsible can't they? Unfortunately one day a real looloo got through her net. It looked innocent enough. It warned him to be careful of his son. "Destiny sees a red sword.", something like that. But she didn't think it mattered because at this point he doesn't have a son and there's a simply marvellous financial forecast ... yes, she thinks he'll ignore what doesn't apply and go on to the good bit. I mean if your horoscope tells you to end a relationship and you are not in one you don't go and start one up just so that you can trash it. Well you don't unless you are my father. He started begetting sons and then eating them, not just the afterbirth, oh no. Mummy was terribly miffed, she'd always wanted a boy, so that when she had a third, yes Zeus my husband, in some ways we were a very close family, she hides him in Granny's bath mat. Well the last place Daddy is going to check up on is his great grandmother's dirty washing pile, isn't it? Mind you he suspected something. He brings in detectives, sniffer dogs and all sorts of complicated equipment but it all gets confused by the Y-fronts and he decides that perhaps he's just getting paranoid and it's been a false pregnancy.

Meanwhile Zeus is being brought up by shepherds on Mount Ida, living on acorns, wild fruit and honey. In some ways it's a very good number. He doesn't have a care in the world and everything is provided for him.

Yes it's a bit like having your parents buy a flat for you and mummy come round once a week to fill up your deep freeze from Marks and Spencers. The trouble is Zeus knows his father is chief god and he feels he's owed something. Daddy doesn't even know he exists which makes him even more resentful, especially as Daddy has begun to notice your lot's compulsion to worship things and is beginning to take an interest in you and do something about the dinosaurs. In exchange for regular sacrifices he even gives some of you work around the palace. Yes, Zeus gets a job as his personal servant. Mummy's never admitted anything but I think she pulled a few strings for him. Nothing was ever proved but I'm sure a jury would find her part in all this very dodgy. Come on, one of Zeus' jobs is mixing Daddy's night time drink. Oh no he doesn't poison him, you are forgetting Gods are immortal. What he does is give him something that makes him very very ill, so ill that he vomits up both Zeus' brothers.

Exactly. Now we have three very disgruntled young gods with huge chips on their shoulders. I know all rich children feel their parents can do more for them, but in this case they do have a point. There is a ten year war, Daddy on the one side, his three sons on the other with you lot supporting them. You are fighting ...

Phone rings

I'm sorry, excuse me a moment.

Picks up phone

Yes ... Juno Casting ... oh it's you again is it? Look dear I said I'd ring you back ... I know you're desperate but there isn't anything you can do about it, is there? ... darling I'm being interviewed by a magazine, it could be very important, I promise I'll ring you back when you're through ... you know that won't do any good ... No promise me you won't ... Why don't you turn yourself into a dog or something, you know you like being a dog ... what is it you said to me? "Because I can." ... Honestly I promise I'll ring you back later ... bye.

Puts down phone

Where were we? Oh yes the war. It seems rather irrelevant now, but we were fighting for liberty and self determination against the massed forces of greed, privilege and expression and Zeus was such a charismatic leader, sharing the hardships of his soldiers, eating with them, sleeping with them, especially if they were female although he wasn't always too particular. There are posters of him with a black headband confronting ... No, I'm not sure exactly what it was he was confronting, just confronting. That was what he was about, confrontation. With all this popular support he was bound to win in the end. Daddy was busy transferring funds into a numbered bank account and one day he just disappeared into exile. We'd won.

The point is Zeus always felt because you'd brought him up

and helped him win the war that there was a special relationship between you, so when everything settled down he moved his base of operations to Mount Olympus.

That's it. That's how you come to be important. So you see horoscopes can be very influential. I'm very surprised you don't run one. Might help you avoid your curse, but then that's all part of the excitement. I wonder what's going to happen to me?

Oh we had to get married. It was expected of us. After all I'd led the Women's Brigade. Oh yes there'd been posters of me too, with a rifle. It was the first big public event of the New Government. There were souvenir urns, little statues of us ... yes and more posters. The ceremony was held at the Acropolis in Athens, they built it specially for us. Just about everybody was there.

I don't know if I loved him. What's love? I mean it's different every relationship, isn't it? We'll have to ask Deedee to give us a definition. I certainly worshipped him. He was Our Leader.

But my husband's childhood does explain such a lot, doesn't it? With our family background it's a wonder we didn't turn out even worse than we did. I mean there was so much inbreeding you have to make allowances for a few eccentrics. The only alternative was sex with the natives, which as you know my husband was rather keen on, used to say he was strengthening the bloodlines which is about the best excuse I've ever heard. It was a very shortsighted policy. It's never a good idea to mess with the workforce. Well people don't worship gods they've slept with, not after the honeymoon period. How can you worship a being who farts in your bed? Anyway it's bad for discipline.

Of course Gods fart darling, there wouldn't be any wind otherwise. That's all weather is, Divine indigestion. The whole reason India has such an odd climate is all those curries. The monsoon season is just excessive indulgence in vindaloo and lager. I tried to have a word with him about it but he felt it was all part of his macho image. Very boring, why he couldn't spend the occasional Saturday night at home with me watching Aristophanes videos I don't know, but there it is, Gods have their yob side just like anyone else.

How do I feel about my husband's infidelities? I wonder how I sort of knew you were going to ask me that one. Perhaps Gods can see into me future after all ... Yes, I know infidelity sells

magazines and his certainly were spectacular, weren't they? ...
The thing that you mustn't forget is that as well as being his wife
I am also his big sister. Yes that does rather complicate things
doesn't it? I sort of come at them from two perspectives.

I mean as his sister I'm expected to be there for him to provide
free counselling about his sex problems, because of course he
can't talk about this kind of thing with his wife ... I know I was
his bloody wife, that was what was so hard. He trusted me to keep
things secret from myself. I did try.

I'd get phone calls in the middle of the night about how he
was in 'lurve' ... yes, he's still at it ... Yes, that was him. Poor
dear he's got no-one else to talk to. I haven't the heart to tell him
I don't owe him anything any more, that would be too cruel. It's
not as if I have to listen, I've got saying 'yes, dear" every ten
minutes down to a fine art, but yes he's still at it even at his age.
Not of course that age is really a problem for gods, but you know
what I mean, you'd think he'd learn from all that experience. No
he keeps making the same mistakes he's always made. Doesn't
seem to have any identity of his own unless he's in a
relationship. He's a great believer in first date sex. It's probably
got something to do with needing to be worshipped. The only
problem is when they do start to worship him he gets bored and
blows them out and we have to start all over again with a new one.
I mean look at his present trouble, it's all his own fault. A very
nice girl called Becky. She worshipped him. Silly girl. He starts
ringing me up to say she's fat and stupid ... Well she's not a size
twelve, not even a Wallis size twelve, but fat's being a bit
unkind, especially as she's exactly the same size she was when
they first got together, and he was keen enough then. Anyway he
ends it. Changes his mind. Changes his mind again, and she goes
off with someone else, which makes her very attractive. Oh no,
she's not fat any more, she's perfect. "I can't live without her"
'I'm so depressed". He's threatening to kill himself, which is
stupid because he's immortal, but it does worry mummy. She
won't go on holiday unless I promise to keep an eye on him and
she needs a break ... oh it'll sort itself out,but I'm sure you
understand being there for him as a sister was one of the main
reasons I left him. I used to get so jealous in the old days, I mean
he never bothered transforming for me ... you must have heard
about his transformations, surely? They were his big thing.

There was a time a girl couldn't get into nice hot bath without checking up first to see if he'd turned himself into the soap or something ... No, I do not exaggerate, poor Leda had a rubber duck. The poor girl's so busy examining the tap she doesn't notice it's grown some additional appendages. Result Helen of Troy, Clytemnestra and the whole Trojan War ... Yes, I know the version you've heard says swan, I assure you it was a duck, you didn't invent journalistic embellishment ... and no it wasn't funny, a disastrous relationship and the next thing to rape in my opinion. Thank god her husband decided against bringing charges, it could have been worse than the O. J. Simpson trial. There'd have been far too much media attention for a fair verdict.

Mind you he did get his come uppance from young Danae. She wasn't exactly for sale but if you weren't a millionaire you might as well not bother. She was very good at saying No ... Yes a real challenge for my husband. After a couple of failures as a peacock and a Siamese cat he decided to try the direct approach and transformed himself into a shower of gold coins. Yes, she spent him, didn't she? One at a time, all over the place. It took him fifty years to get back together and we were never quite sure that some of the coins hadn't got lost. He used to have terrible memory lapses. Honestly it would only have taken one of the girls lodging a complaint with the authorities and he could have been in serious trouble. If poor Mike Tyson can be committed on a lot less evidence he wouldn't have stood a chance. I mean we were in mid term and carrying out a lot of unpopular policies. We'd just stopped public human sacrifice and slapped a massive tax on temple prostitution. No, you lot weren't at all happy with us. A nice juicy scandal about divine sleaze could have had us all out of our jobs. He never used condoms, said he was allergic to sheepskin. That's what they were made of in those days. They were sewn by shepherdesses because their simple shepherd swains wouldn't make love without them, well not to shepherdesses.

Of course there was an opposition. There were all those gods who'd chosen the wrong thing to be god of, like Araldite. She came unstuck very badly. She'd thought with Grecian urns as popular as they were she was onto a good thing, but after all what's a Grecian urn? ... I know, I know depends where he works ... but seriously they were so easy to make they weren't worth mending, so she never made the big time, well not then anyway. I'm told there are some people these days who swear by her.

No, honestly, I'm not trying to avoid your question, darling. It's just it's so difficult to remember what I felt like when I was his wife. I've sort of blocked it out. You do with past relationships. I mean we've been separated for over two thousand years, now. I was another person then ... Come on are you the same person you were ten years ago. Some of the things you did then are definitely best forgotten ... Yes, him ... No dear, I'm not being omniscient, I gave up being omniscient years ago, but it was a good guess wasn't it? We've all got our bits of past we don't want to be reminded of ... Well then, can't I be forgiven the way I used to overreact two thousand years ago. I was young and passionate. I mean what would you do if you came home and found your partner and a girl with no clothes on playing dungeons and dragons?

I will say that whatever he may claim now, I never agreed to an open marriage. No way. They never work out. It's not really very nice trying to sleep next to a man who's spent the afternoon in another girl's bath skulking behind the soap pretending to be a rubber duck. Anne Summers has a lot to answer for.

But I do think that at the time I got rather an unfair press. Mind you all the reporters were men so of course they were on his side. He was one of the lads. You certainly wouldn't have got a job then, women with literary pretensions were considered very unnatural. Look at the trouble poor Sappho had and she almost was one of the lads.

No I'd get a lot more sympathy and support today, wouldn't I? and I'd definitely get custody of the children. I did a lot of charity work, you know ... Oh yes if it hadn't been for Save the Trojans all those boat people would have starved and the relocation of the Atlanteans after the disaster was one of my proudest moments.

Oh Atlantis isn't just a myth, darling. It was between you and America, wonderful beaches, the playground of the gods, What makes me so angry is its destruction could so easily have been avoided. Diana and I tried to start a movement to ban the testing of new weapons technology, It became ever so trendy. We had a sort of uniform, well a uniform in the sense that it was what we all wore, we were far too alternative for a uniform, of woollen capes with hoods and wooden buttons and a sign rather like a penis, well weapons are so masculine, aren't they? There were rallies and marches from Athens to Sparta, all the philosophers were on our side ... No a complete waste of energy, Mars and my husband refused to sign the agreement and before you know it a very minor deity called Epimetheos ... exactly, you've never heard of him, that's how minor he was, is testing an underwater fire catapult. He was warned what could happen but he wouldn't listen and of course it set off a couple of volcanoes and that was the end of Atlantis and Epimetheos.

But you don't get any of this in Robert Graves' Greek Myths, do you? It would show women in far too sensible a light. What you get is a very biassed account of my treatment of young Dionysos and his mother ... Have you ever met the man? A complete anorak, when he's not drunk or stoned he's being incredibly boring about dramatic forms. Honestly he makes Stanislavski seem exciting and he hates actresses, feels all the female parts should be played by men.

But yes, I still think Gods have a role to play in the twenty first century. Mind you we're going to have to be a lot more democratic if we are to survive. Consensus manifestation, that's what's needed. There isn't really a place for arbitrary ineffability any more. You see I think if you had a poll you'd find most people like to have some sort of hereditary god. It gives them a sense of security and of course it stops power getting into the wrong hands. I mean what's the alternative? An elected deity? What would you get then? A retired politician? a pop star? People wouldn't know where they were. I can just imagine the elections. All sorts of promises of miracles and revelations and then once they were in power punitive sacrifice in order to pay for them. You can't have welfare miracles unless you've got a sound economic base to start with. Much better the way things are, we're good for the tourist industry if nothing else. I mean look how well Rome does out of us? It's not only the Vatican and St Peters and all that, I've still got a couple of temples that attract a great many visitors every year. Oh and a rest home for cats in one of the forums. I mean communism tried to do without us, didn't it? And look what happened to it. Ah no, you lot still need gods, mind you you could do with a few new ones, there's no doubt the internet needs someone to keep it under control.

That would be the ultimate challenge for Juno Casting wouldn't it? Selecting the right people for things that need gods. They'd have to be very carefully screened, and if what we were doing leaked out the phone would never stop ringing ... yes, she'd be worse than my ex, wouldn't she? She used to think she was a god when she was in control and she's certainly not satisfied with a seat in the House of Lords.

Phone rings

Oh no, I hope she hasn't overheard us ... just joking, it'll be him again, he's so impatient. Sorry, I'd better answer it.

Picks up phone

Look I told you ... Oh Granny I'm sorry, I thought ... oh, he's rung you, has he? ... Yes, Becky ... Look Granny he's nothing to do with me any more ... well, yes I am still his sister ... yes, I know that but I don't see what I can do about it, I took early retirement remember ... oh Granny you are being a little prejudiced ... it's not as if it is the first time ... I think that would be rather drastic ... you can't do that Granny ... Yes, I know it would solve his problem but where would we all go, I've just written a book ... Thank you, it's doing very well, yes I'll send you a copy ... I see, I suppose if you've made up your mind there's nothing I can say then, is there? ... goodbye.

Puts down phone

Sorry about that, it was my grandmother ... yes the bathmat lady ... Isn't there something about there being a sort of curse on the people you interview? ... oh no, I'm going to be all right ... It's just that well, my ex husband's upset granny with all this Becky business and she feels it''s about time she washed that bathmat.

Fade to black
Sound of washing machine starting.